Secondary Complications Associated with Down S

Chandreswara Raju Kataru

Secondary Complications Associated with Down Syndrome

First Edition February 2024

Written by Chandreswara Raju Kataru

Index

SL. No	Content	Page No.

List of Figures

List of Tables

ABBREVIATIONS

A.a: Amino acid

AD: Alzheimer's disease

ALL: Acute Lymphocytic Leukemia

AML: Acute Myeloid Leukemia

AMKL: Acute Megakaryoblastic leukemia

APC: Activated Protein C

APCR: Activated Protein C Resistance

APOE: Apolipoprotein E

APP: Amyloid Precursor Protein

AUTS2: Activator of Transcription and Developmental Regulator

AVSD: Atrio Ventricular Septal Defect

BMF: Bone Marrow Failure

BACE2: Beta secretase 2

BWA: Burrows-Wheeler Alignment

CHD: Congenital Heart Disease

CLL: Chronic Lymphocytic Leukemia

CML: Chronic Myeloid Leukemia

CNOT3: CCR4-NOT Transcription Complex Subunit 3

COL6A3: Collagen Type VI Alpha 3 Chain

CRELD1: Cystine Rich Epidermal growth-factor Like Domain

C V: Co-efficient of variability

D.H$_2$O: Distilled water

DIC: Disseminated intravascular coagulopathy

DNA: Deoxyribo nucleic acid

d NTP mix: di Nucleotide Triphosphate mix

DS: Down Syndrome

DS-ALL: DS -Acute Lymphoblastic Leukemia

DSCAM: Down Syndrome cell adhesion molecule

DVT: Deep vein thrombosis

EDTA: Ethylenediamine tetra acetic acid

ELB: Erythrocyte Lysis Buffer

ETV6: ETS Variant Transcription Factor 6

FISH: Fluorescence in Sensitive Hybridization

FLT3: FMS-like Tyrosine Kinase 3

FVL: Factor V Leiden

GATK: Genomic Analysis Tool Kit

GIP-1: Gastric Inhibitory Polypeptide

GLP-1: Glucagon Like Polypeptide

HD: Hirschsprung's Disease

IA: Imperforate anus

IKZF1: IKAROS Family Zinc Finger 1

INDEL: Insertion/ Deletion

JAK2: Janus kinase 2

KCEN4: Potassium voltage-gated channel subfamily E member 4

KMT2A: Lysine Methyltransferase 2A

MLPA: Multiplex Probe Ligation Assay

MTHF: Methylene tetrahydrofolate

MTHFR: Methylene Tetra Hydro Folate Reductase

ML-DS: Myeloid leukemia of Down syndrome

NDIC: Nigeria deposit insurance corporation

NGS: Next generation Sequence

NIDDK: National Institute of diabetes and digestive disorder

NMD: Nonsense-Mediated mRNA decay

ANOVA: One-way analysis of variance

PAI-1: Plasminogen Activator Inhibitor-1

PAX5: Paired box5

PCR-RFLP: Polymerase chain reaction- Restriction fragment length polymorphism

PE: Pulmonary Embolism

PICALM: Phosphatidylinositol binding Clathrin assembly protein

PDGFRA: Platelet-derived growth factor receptor alpha

PSQ: Paralogous sequence quantification

QF-PCR: Quantitative Fluorescence Polymerase Chain Reaction

RNA: Ribonucleic acid

Rnase: Ribonuclease

SALL2: Spalt Like Transcription Factor 2

SNP: Single Nucleotide Polymorphism

T1DM: Type 1 Diabetes Mellitus

T2DM: Type 2 Diabetes Mellitus

TAL1: T-cell acute leukemia 1

TCL1A: TCL1 Family AKT Coactivator A

TCF3: Transcription Factor 3

TMD: Transient myeloproliferative disorder

TP53: Tumour suppressor Protein 53

TE buffer: Tris-EDTA buffer

TRH: Thyrotropin Releasing Hormone

TSH: Thyroid Stimulating Hormone

VEP: Variant Effect Predictor

VTE: Venous Thrombo Embolism

VSD: Ventricular Septal Defect

WBC: White Blood Cells

WHO: World Health Organisation

INTRODUCTION

1. INTRODUCTION

1.1.Down syndrome:

Down syndrome (DS) is a most common human congenital anomaly with several physical and mental traits, caused by an extra chromosome present on 21st chromosome, also known as trisomy 21 (Lejeune J 1959). Trisomy 21 is caused by abnormal segregation during meiosis with around 90% cases of mothers with the incidence of 1 in 800 live births (Roizen NJ 2003). There is an increased tendency of miscarriage with trisomic fetuses, thus the DS patients develop various medical conditions (Morris JK.1999). In developed countries the life expectancy of the DS has increased up to 55 years with advance in medical treatment (Glasson EJ 2002). An extra maternal chromosome involves predominantly 90% of trisomic conditions, mainly due to meiotic errors in the egg (Hassold T 2000). In humans the frequent cause of fetal death is due to the chromosomal abnormality. Within the initial 15 weeks of gestation period, half of the spontaneous abortions are chromosomally aneuploid, and approximately 50% of trisomies occurs due to spontaneous abortions (Hassold T 1980). In newborns, due to the high incident rate, autosomal trisomies 21, 18, 13 occur large in number along with social and economic complications (Hassold T 1984). Though the biological mechanisms are yet to understand, advanced mothers' age has a potential role in non-disjunction (Penrose LS 1933). Down syndrome was first identified with mongoloid facial features by John Lang Down in 1866 for which he earned the name of "father of Down syndrome". Later in 1959, Lejeune - Gautier –Turpin identified Down syndrome as a genetic abnormality with the presence of 47 chromosomes, instead of usual 46 chromosomes (Lejeune J 1959). When the initial sequence of 21 q was published, a total of 225 genes were listed. The dosage imbalance of genes located on the human chromosome 21 is influenced by the several phenotypic features of the DS. Experimental evidences indicate that single gene dosage imbalance can cause several abnormal phenotypes (Lettice, LA 2003). The length of the 21q is 33.5 Mb (Lyle R 2009) and the 21 p is 5-15 Mb (Ermak G 2006). Depending on the size of the triplicated genome, trisomies are classified into four types as complete or whole chromosome trisomies, partial trisomies, micro trisomies and single gene duplication (Antonarakis SE 2004).

1.1.1. Complete or whole chromosome trisomies: In this condition, a complete chromosome is present and it occurs through the event called meiotic or mitotic non disjunction, which accounts for 0.3- 0.5% DS cases. Trisomies are frequently seen in spontaneous abortions; the incidence of trisomy 16 is 1 in 13 and trisomy 21 is 1 in 43 (Hsu LY 1998).

1.1.2. Partial trisomies: Partial trisomies are less frequent than whole chromosome trisomies and the genomic region of more than one chromosomal band will be larger than 5Mb. This condition arises with abnormal meiosis and segregation in an individual with balanced chromosomal rearrangements. The half of the partial trisomies are unbalanced, non-Robertsonian rearrangements which occurs 1 in 800 new-borns, unbalanced Robertsonian translocations with trisomies of acrocentric chromosomes which occur 1 in 14,000 new-borns.

1.1.3. Micro trisomies: This condition is evidenced by the presence of partial trisomy 21 with the genomic region of less than 3 Mb in size. This occurs due to unequal crossovers in meiosis, which is mediated by the low copy numbers or inter chromosomal duplications. The incidence of micro trisomies are still unknown.

1.1.4. Single gene duplication: The duplication or triplication of a single gene or functional genomic element occurs in this condition. It is a type of mutation and arises during homologous recombination. Gene duplications can encompass the additional sequences and it can cause diseases. Experimental evidences in transgenic mice indicate that abnormal phenotype may arise due to gene duplications. (Readhead C 1994 & Magyar JP 1996).

The clinical phenotype of Down syndrome is complex and highly variable, it varies from one to another (Epstein CJ 1989). Features like muscle hypotonia, cognitive impairment

11

and dysmorphic features have been observed at birth. In some of the individuals with DS, several other traits like difficulty in walking, speaking and learning disabilities were also observed. The published literatures suggest that phenotypic traits may vary in DS (Roizen NJ 2003).

Individuals with DS are more prone to develop secondary complications such as neurological defects, cardiovascular defects, thrombosis, diabetes, leukemia, etc. Occurrence of such complications are four times higher in DS compared to that of individuals with non-DS (Epstein LG 1991).

1.2. Diabetes and Cardiovascular complications:

Diabetes is most prominent disease among the world, and it occurs when the blood glucose levels are exceptionally high. The blood glucose level is maintained by insulin hormone which is secreted by the pancreas. Diabetes is classified into different types as type 1, type 2 and gestational diabetes. Type 1 Diabetes is known as insulin dependent diabetes and it begins during childhood, thus also named as juvenile onset diabetes. Various health complications are associated with type 1 Diabetes such as diabetic retinopathy, neuropathy and nephropathy. Type 1 diabetes has a higher risk of occurrence of stroke and heart disease. Type 2 diabetes, the most common diabetes, is known as insulin independent diabetes, also named as adult-onset diabetes. The insulin production in these individuals may be insufficient or cells do not respond. Gestational diabetes is developed during pregnancy and it causes insulin resistance.

Diabetes mellitus demonstrates metabolic disorder of various factors identified by chronic hyperglycaemia with dysfunction of various metabolic pathways like carbohydrate, fat and protein metabolisms results of the dysfunction of both insulin secretion and action. The diabetes mellitus effects include prolonged damage, failure and dysfunction of various organs.

12

Previous studies suggest increased prevalence of type 1 Diabetes in individuals with Down syndrome (Milunsky A 1968; Bergholdt R 2006). Congenital Heart Disease (CHD) affects the walls and valves of the heart. CHD is the most prominent leading cause of death in the first 2 years of the Down syndrome individuals (Levenson D 2009 & Freeman SB 1998). The incidence rate of CHD in DS new-borns is up to 50% (Urbano R 2012).

1.3. Thrombophilia:

A coagulation system generally having a balanced homeostatic mechanism in between the Pro and Anti Coagulation. Upon injury, the coagulation cascade is stimulated and forms fibrin mesh. Anticoagulation pathway controls the coagulation with the help of Activated Protein C (APC) and it specifically cleaves the Factor Va and VIII a. (Van Cott EM 2002 & Bloomenthal D 2002).

The interconversion of Homeostasis in to Procagulation condition results in (uncontrolled blood clot) Thrombosis or this condition is known as Thrombophilia. (Ornstein DL 2003). Depends on the site of clot formation thrombophilia will be known as venous and Arterial thrombosis. It may be either acquired or hereditary (Kutteh WH 2006). Venous thrombosis comprise pulmonary Embolism (PE) and Deep Venous Thrombosis (DVT) (Lane DA 1996). The genetic risk factors of Venous Thromboembolism (VTE) are assessed by both qualitative and quantitative abnormalities of Protein C and Protein S and anti-thrombin levels (Svensson PJ 1994). Generally Venous Thrombosis can arise from Hyper-active anticoagulant pathways and hypoactive anticoagulant mechanisms or hypoactive fibrinolysis (Miletich JP 1993). Thrombosis is most predominant disease leads to death in the western countries. Thrombosis (both venal and arterial) disease progression of disruption the normal homeostatic balance. Haemostasis can be maintained in healthy population by various anti-coagulant mechanisms and balance the pro-coagulant forces, it will stop unwanted blood clotting. In the haemostasis process slight dominance can be seen in the anticoagulant forces by various factors

(Dhalback B 2000) the risk factors for VTE includes both hereditary and acquired factors, the hereditary factors which includes Protein S and protein C anti-thrombin deficiency, Factor V Leiden gene, prothrombin gene, MTHFR gene mutations, plasminogen deficiency, factor XII deficiency and Dysfibrinogenemia's, the Acquired factors includes Surgery, Elderly Trauma, especially orthopaedic Immobilisation, Long distance travel, Obesity, Pregnancy and puerperium, oral contraceptives and hormone replacement therapy, Malignancy, Disseminated intravascular coagulopathy (DIC), chemotherapy, tamoxifen, central venous catheter, Heparin Induced Thrombocytopenia, Congenital heart failure, Nephrotic syndrome, Antiphospholipid Antibody syndrome, Myeloproliferative disorders (Polycythaemia vera; Essential Thrombocytopenia), Hyper viscosity, Paroxysmal nocturnal haemoglobinuria, Sickle cell anemia and other.

1.4. Hematological malignancy or Leukemia:

Leukemia defines an abnormal/uncontrolled production of bone marrow and blood producing organs. Leukemia is broadly classified into acute and chronic. Depending on the type of blood cells affect malignancy can be classified into myeloid leukemia, which affects myeloid cells and in the lymphoid leukemia lymphocytes will affect. In the haematopoietic process both types of haematopoietic cells (myeloid and lymphoid) are produced (Kondo M 2010).

Myeloid cells of granulocytes (eosinophils, basophils and neutrophils) and monocytes (granulocytes) effects by the malignancy this type of leukemia known as myeloid leukemia and whereas T & B lymphoid cells affects by the malignancy will be known as lymphocytic leukemia (Haouas H 2010) Leukemia is of different types among them 4 are very important types these include Acute Myeloid Leukemia (AML), Chronic Myeloid Leukemia (CML), Acute Lymphocytic Leukemia (ALL) and Chronic Lymphocytic Leukemia (CLL) (Redaelli A 2003).

14

Precisely chronic forms of Leukemia will gradually modify to acute forms which are most dangerous. People with genetic disorders like Down syndrome, Li – Fraumeni syndrome, neurofibromatosis, bloom syndrome, Fanconi anemia, Diamond-Blackfan anemia and several others are prone to develop leukemia (Xavier AC 2010).

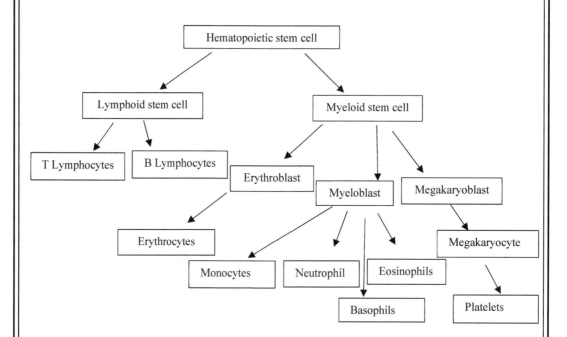

Figure-1. **Hematopoiesis mechanism.** It represents both Lymphoid and Myeloid stem cells, a multipotent hematopoietic stem cells into the broad division of myeloid stem cell and Lymphoid stem cells. In particular to Down syndrome, lymphoblasts have seen in DS -acute lymphoblastic leukemia (Ds-ALL) are originated from lymphoid stem cells. And where as megakaryoblasts originated from myeloid stem cells. Transient myeloproliferative disorder (TMD), a pre leukemic condition and myeloid leukemia of Down syndrome (ML-DS) are both conditions by the defective megakaryoblast (Marion K 2015).

15

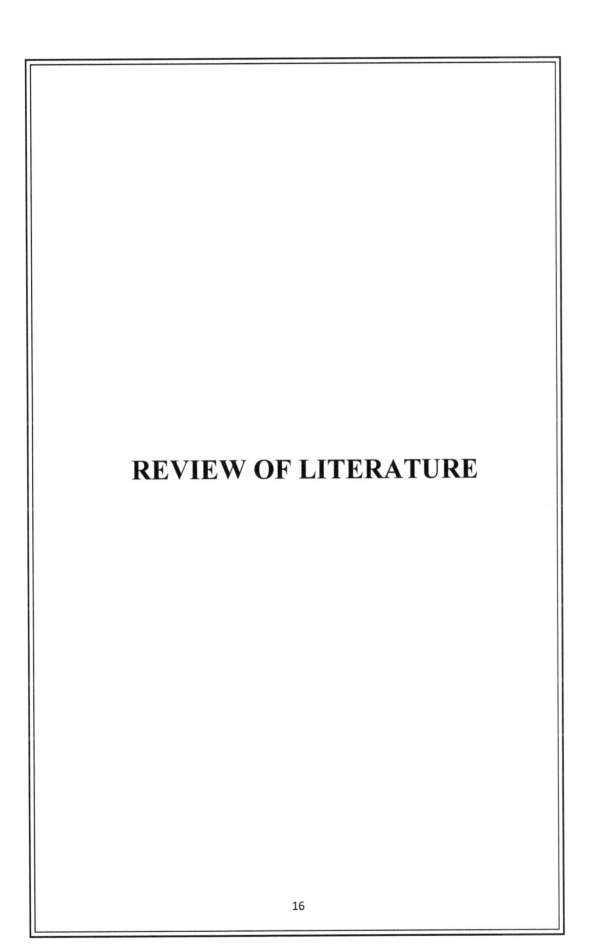

REVIEW OF LITERATURE

2. REVIEW OF LITERATURE

2.1 Human Trisomy 21:

The effectiveness of each phenotypic character differs from one another and hence identification of each Single Nucleotide Polymorphism (SNP) on the Human chromosome 21 helps the understanding of phenotypic variability to genotypic variability (Deutsch G 2001). With improved advances in medical treatment and social care the DS life span is increased up to 60 years (Bittles AH 2004). With an extra copy of human chromosome 21, most of the genes over express, and leads to the differentiation of expression of several genes in different tissues (Prandini P 2007; Yahya-Graison EA 2007; Sultan M 2007). In the 1950 Waardenburg and Davenport invented the technique called karyotyping to study chromosome structure within individuals of cells. Hence, this study was open the doors to study chromosomes and their abnormalities (Megarbane A 2009).

2.2 Genetic Mechanisms of DS:

Genes are present in the chromosomes, alongside egg and sperm cell's chromosomes contains 23 pairs identical chromosomes, a total 46 chromosomes, which include 22 pairs of autosomes and one pair of allosomes/Sex chromosomes. The chromosomes have arranged from 1 to 22 depending on their size. In meiosis, while the egg cells progress, very rarely in sperm cells errors may occur at segregation step. This error results, improper separation of chromosomes also known as chromosomal non-disjunction, leads to egg or sperm cells chances of getting separated 22 or 24 chromosomes respectively. Along with cell division the extra chromosome will divides in all the cells of the body, the extra chromosome present in all the body cells known as trisomy 21 (Ahmed M 2010, Ghosh S 2015; Noble J 1998, Sherman SL 2007).

In human cell division of first meiosis mechanism involves pairing, recombination and segregation. The pairing process includes paring off 2 parental chromosomes and locate to each other. Second step genetic recombination involves the exchange of genetic material within the paired homologous pairs. Third step chromosomal segregation includes at the metaphase stage each of the chromosome pair separate from their partners. Intern leads a formation of 23 pairs of chromosomes in the segregation process (Ghosh S 2015 & Hassold T 2002). A normal gamete either a sperm or ova cell merges with unusual gamete (chromosome number is abnormal) results in the formation of unusual gamete with the 47 chromosomes instead of the 46 chromosomes. The extra chromosome can cause the unusual progression of cells, which leads to the person's intellectual disabilities and medical and physical abnormalities with trisomy 21 (Ghosh S 2015, Noble J 1998, Sherman SL 2007, & Hassold T 2007).

2.3 Features of Down syndrome:

Certain physical and behavioural features are common to all DS patients that include craniofacial abnormality, learning disability, difficulty in walking and speaking, hypotonia, and physical characteristics like short fingers, slanted eyes, flat nasal bridge, small mouth and protruding tongue, poor muscle tone and several other.

2.3.1 Intellectual Disability (ID): Intellectual disability is common in children with Down syndrome will learn slowly and progress than the other children due to developmental delay. This ID will be represented as below average intelligence and lack of necessary skills to lead a regular life. People with ID learn slowly when compared with normal people, and they will learn with special skills and do fast.

2.3.2. Hypotonia: People with DS develop hypotonia. In this condition healthy muscles relaxed; this condition named as poor muscle tone. People with this hypotonic condition, difficulty in the movement (Faulks D 2008). People with COL6A3 SNP association with muscular Hypotonia in patients with Down syndrome (Dey A 2013).

2.4 Secondary Complications associated with Down syndrome:

Down syndrome is associated with more than 80 clinical traits, along with physical and behavioural traits which includes cardiac problems, childhood leukemia, Alzheimer's disease immune disorders and several others (Epstein LG 1991).

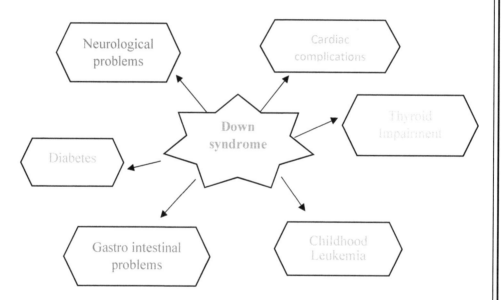

Figure-2.1: Complications associated with Down syndrome.

2.4.1 Cardiac Complications:

The most prominent cardiac defect in DS children's is Atrio Ventricular Septal Defect (AVSD) and its 40% common form of cardiac defect (Asim A 2015) it's associated with CRELD1 gene mutations of Non Hsa-21 genes and another most common cardiac defect is seen in 30% DS children is Ventricular Septal Defect (VSD) (Wiseman FK 2009). The cell

19

adhesion molecule Cysteine Rich Epidermal growth-factor Like Domain (CRELD 1) is present on chromosome 3 and its mutations influence the genetic mechanism of CHD in Down syndrome population (Priestly MD 2000). Pulmonary arterial hypertension is highly expected condition in patients with Down syndrome, whether they may have CHD and without CHD. Which includes various factors, but mostly due to large incidence of CHD and most prominently airway problems (Consisting of the voice, throat box, and trachea) plays an active role in the progression (D'Alto M 2012).

2.4.2 Diabetes:

Previous studies suggest that, there's an increased tendency to develop diabetes mellitus in Down syndrome population along with autoimmune disorders such as autoimmune thyroiditis and Celiac disease. Even though these studies are reported highly increased risk factors of Diabetes mellitus in Ds, but there are limitations they couldn't differentiate the different forms of Diabetes mellitus (Milunsky A 1968; Jeremeah DE 1973). And another study reveals that 1.7%-fold increased risk of developing diabetes with a training centre who attended the Down syndrome patients and with no differentiation of T1DM and T2DM (Jeremeah DE 1973). Another recent study from Dutch reveals that 3 times increased risk of developing both T1DM and T2DM (VanGoor JC 1997). The recent study demonstrates that 4.2% increase prevalence of T1DM with Down syndrome population (Bergholdt R 2006).

2.4.3 Hypothyroidism:

Hypothyroidism is a condition where enough thyroid synthesis doesn't produce from the thyroid gland for the regular body needs. And it mainly involves in metabolism and regulates and influences nearly every organ. Previous studies suggest that with low amounts of thyroid synthesis body function slows down, 4.2 % of people have the hypothyroidism at the age of 12 years and more has hypothyroidism. The thyroid can be supplied through thyroid

20

hormones, mainly these are 2 types T3 and T4, produced by Thyroid gland. This thyroid gland is located beside neck and It's regulated by another master endocrine gland called Pituitary gland. Thyroid hormone levels in the blood are 99% T4 and whereas T3 is 1% respectively. Thyroid hormones released form thyroid gland into the blood stream T4 are converted into T3. Its active form and plays a role in biological activity.

Thyroid hormones also regulated by Hypothalamus. It's a part of the brain and plays an active role in thyroid release. The hypothalamus releases the Thyrotropin Releasing Hormone (TRH), it's sends the signal to the pituitary gland to release the Thyroid Stimulating Hormone (TSH). Thyroid gland gets the signal to release thyroid hormones by TSH. Any disturbance at any of these steps causes the disruption of thyroid hormone production which leads to Hypothyroidism. Thyroid hormone production regulated by feed mechanism of pituitary gland TSH. In Hypothyroidism condition, there are low levels of thyroid hormones in the circulation.

The association of Down syndrome and hypothyroidism have explained previously, the prevalence rate of the DS with congenital hypothyroidism and acquired thyroid dysfunction. (Pueschel SM 1985; Fort P 1984; Karlsson B 1998). In previous studies the congenital hypothyroidism in patients with Down syndrome is 28 times more than the normal population (Fort P 1984). The reported prevalence of Hypothyroidism in children with Down syndrome is 4-18%. An early detection of hypothyroidism in children with Down syndrome will decrease the risk of intellectual disabilities and prevent additional risk (Bull MJ 2011).

2.4.4. Thrombophilic Complications:

Thrombophilia is an abnormal condition, it may be genetic or acquired condition characterise normal individual into Venous or arterial Thrombosis (Kutteh WH 2006). Contemporary studies suggest that hereditary thrombophilia is involved in several complications among them recurrent pregnancy loss is the major one (Bozikova A 2015). In vivo experimental evidences clearly indicate that inadequate amount of methyl and dietary folate consequences Hypomethylation (Pogribny IP 1997; Chritman JK 1993). Deterioration of DNA strands and results abnormal gene expression (Pogribny IP 1995 & 1997; Wainfan E 1992). VTE may be either genetic or acquired and the risk factors increase the frequency (Alfirevic Z 2010). The frequently recognised mutations of VTE are MTHFR 667 C>T; FVL 1691 G>A; Prothrombin A 20210 G>A and Protein S and Protein C, Antithrombin III.

2.4.4.1. Methylene Tetra hydro Folate Reductase (MTHFR):

MTHFR 677 C>T variation is one of the confined genetic risk factors for maternal meiotic non-disjunction (James SJ 1999) in the DS. MTHFR gene is located on chromosome $1p36.22$, this gene having 19 transcript variants and 12 exons. In exon 4 the 677 C>T variation interferes Cysteine metabolism and the aetiology and prevalence has been described (Tosetto A 1997). This specific MTHFR enzyme and its variations and mechanism in association of folate cycle and these effects on DNA methylation has been explained (Fodinger M 2000; Lucock M 2000 & 2004; Cicek MS 2004). MTHFR plays a critical role in regulation of cellular methylation reactions (Frosst P. et.al. 1995). And involves in the conversion of 5,10 Methylene Tetrahydrofolate to 5 Methyl tetrahydrofolates, provides methyl groups (James SJ 1999).

In MTHFR more than 40 polymorphisms have reported, though 667C>T (rs 1801133; ALA 222 VAL) variant is predominantly studied and clinically reported. And in association with increased homo cysteine levels and decrease MTHFR activity. (Frosst P 1995; Bagley PJ 1998). The defective MTHFR leads to decrease levels of SAM then subsequently DNA hypomethylation (Wainfan E 1992; De Cabo SF 1994; Balaghi M 1993).

22

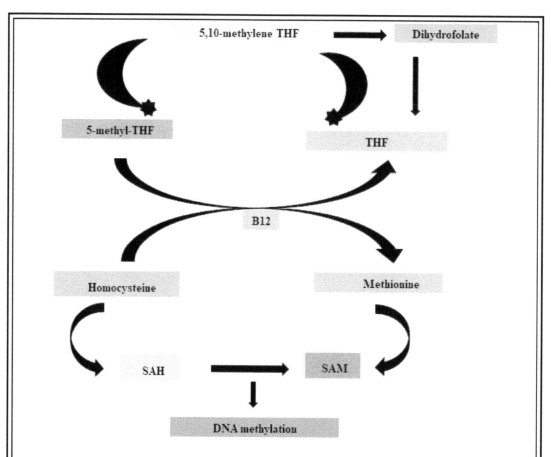

Figure-2.2: MTHFR Metabolism and DNA methylation. Source (James J 1999)

The MTHFR gene C677T variant is a point mutation with the replacement with the subsequent nucleotide of Cystine to Thymine it leads to the replacement of Alanine to Valine in the MTHFR gene (Rosenberg et.al.2002). The meta-analysis report suggests that the MTHFR C677T variant enhance the risk of hemorrhagic stroke. This specific variant involves in the myocardial infarction in young and middle-aged population and also be reported on the potential risk of coronary heart disease (Klerk M 2002).

Atypical folate metabolism leads to a risk factor of Down syndrome (James SJ 1999). And the more relevant association of MTHFR C 677 T variation and promotes the risk of Down syndrome offspring's and suggest with meta-analysis report this specific variation is associated with Parkinson's Disease. MTHFR C 677 T variant has an association with Infertility and recurrent pregnancy loss. This specific variant has an association with Alzheimer's disease in

23

a different set of population (Hua Y 2011). MTHFR C 677 T variant has a role in the combination of psychiatric disorders-Schizophrenia, Unipolar Depressive disorder, and bipolar disorder (Gilbody S 2007; Peerbooms OL 2011). With modern meta-analysis reports this specific variation has a high risk of Schizophrenia and bipolar diseases. MTHFR specific variant has an association with several cancers.

2.4.4.2. Factor V Leiden (FVL):

Factor V is a protein, it is involved in the blood clotting mechanism, when injury or tissue damage occurs. Factor V Leiden represents a mutation in the Factor V and its atypical kind of Factor V and it makes APC inactive, results APC can't prevent the Fibrin formation (Deborah L 2003). FVL is the most prevalent genetic risk factor with 50% for familial thrombophilia and 20 to 25% of VTE (Dahlback B 1993). Commonly, people with DVT have no symptoms and signs, but these symptoms can be measured depending on the vessel inflammation and obstruction levels. Thrombophilia is one of the major factors in case of pregnant mother and children at young age, it can be diagnosed with the help of FVL mutation screening by which PCR-RFLP and Activated Protein C Resistance (APCR) (Zehnder JL 1996). Among which molecular technique RFLP- PCR methods are expensive and difficult to perform time consuming as well.

Factor V Leiden gene is located on chromosome *1q24.2,* and it's having 25 exons at the 10 exon a single point mutation where Adenine replaces Guanine at position 1691. This variant results in the formation of Glutamine to Arginine at the position of 506, consequently resulted protein prevent the cleavage of Factor V with the help of APC and results detain the inactivation and clotting process will become less prohibited, leads to Venous Thromboembolism. A meta-analysis report states that 1691 G →A variation adults' patients has reported with the Venous Thromboembolism (Marjot T 2011). 3 to 7 folds increased

24

chances of getting VTE with Heterozygous mutation oof FVL and whereas 80-fold increased

rare with a homozygous mutation (Ridker PM 1995; Rosendaal FR 1995).

The FVL mutation plays a major role in Cerebral Venous Thrombosis and Artery Ischemic

Stroke (Beye A 2017).

2.4.4.3. Prothrombin:

Prothrombin gene is located on chromosome *11p 11- q 12* and it's having 14 exons and

separated by 13 introns with the 5 prime upstream untranslated regions and 3 prime UTR

(untranslated region), G to A transition at the 20210 position which plays a major role in gene

expression. (Degen SJF 1987.) This variation increases the plasma prothrombin levels and

increases the Venous Thrombo Embolism complications. (Poort SR 1996). Geographical

variations have observed in this specific mutation. The frequency is very high in the general

population of Europe and Middle East (Bavikatty N 2000), and whereas in Africans and Asians

are very less (Katcharin A 2012).

The inherited causes of the Thrombophilia and Venous Thrombo Embolism (VTE) are

FVL 1691 G>A and Prothrombin 20210 G>A variations. The FVL heterozygous mutation 4-

to-8-fold increased risk factor and whereas the Homozygous mutation is having 80-fold

increased risk factor for VTE. (Bloomenthal D 2002; Horne MDK 2006; Libby EN 2005;

Kabukcu S 2007; Wilmer M 2004.) Even though the FVL mutations are found in the healthy

case of Indian frequency and where it's not widely different from the Europe (Kumar SI 2005).

The 20210 G> A transition will increase the VTE risk by 3 folds. (Huber S 2000). Moreover,

this study demonstrates the G 20210 A mutation other than Europe and where as the only case

found among 22 non- European countries that case from India (Rees DC 1999). Experimental

evidences suggest that the Prothrombin gene 20210 mutation plays a major role in cerebral

sinus venous thrombosis (Beye A 2017).

The reported meta-analysis studies suggest that the role MTHFR C 677 T variant increases the risk of VTE (Gohil R 2009). And the Risk of VTE can increase the MTHFR C677T along with the FVL G1691A and Prothrombin G 20210 A mutations.

2.4.5. Hematological Complications:

Leukemia represents the cancer of human body, blood forming tissues which include Bone marrow and Lymphatic system. Leukemia remains various types some forms of leukemia exist in children's and some forms exist in adults. Leukemia begins in the White Blood Cells (WBC), in general WBC's are strongly protected the body against infection, by organising normal grow and divide as per the body's requirement and where in case of leukemia body produces abnormal number of WBC's and which do not function properly. The general symptoms of Leukemia will vary depends on the type of leukemia, which includes common symptoms are Fever or chill, losing weight, frequent and severe infections, recurrent nasal bleeding, Liver or spleen enlargement, swollen lymph nodes, weakness and frequent fatigue, Bone pain or tenderness and several others.

The general risk factors of Leukemia include previous cancer treatments which includes chemotherapy, radiation therapy and certain genetic disorders like Fanconi anemia and Down syndrome. And due to few blood disorders like Myelodysplastic syndromes, certain radiation exposure, smoking, family history of leukemia. Cancer susceptibility remains elusive due to germ line mutations. Leukemia progress is mainly linked with Genetic or clinical syndromes such as Fanconi anemia, Congenita dyskeratosis, Trisomy 21. Previous reports suggest that the germline hereditary mutations play an important role in the cancer development in the carriers. Many of these genetic variations are associated with Leukemia and increase prevalence of pathogens. Several sequencing techniques have helped to find this variation. By using dispassionate and targeted sequence's will help the understanding of genetic syndromes and

26

their involvement in the pathogenesis of hematological malignancy of the patients (Christoph.C 2016).

2.4.5.1. Syndromic tendency into leukemia:

Various syndromes have notified on the development of leukemia for several years. And the best example is Fanconi anemia is an autosomal recessive factor and eventually it causes bone marrow failure (BMF), short stature and primarily develops leukemia acute myeloid leukemia (AML). Nineteen different DNA damaging genes lead to the development of Fanconi anemia (Duxin JP 2015). The Fa genes BRACA 1 and BRACA 2 with an association of Ovarian-Breast cancer syndromes, and these genes hereditably mutated along with some DNA damage repair genes found to be in 20% of patients related with therapeutic treatments (Schulz.E 2012; Churpek JE 2016).

Uniformly due to the mutations of telomeric maintenance genes (TERC, DKC1 and TINF2) in dyskeratosis Congenita patients develops BMF and high frequency rate to develop AML (Alter BP 2009). Due to trisomy 21 DS patients show phenotypic features and congenital heart diseases and development of Leukemia both ALL and AML. The incidences of ALL and AML is 33 and 150 times higher with a normal age matched control. According to the World Health Organisation (WHO), in neonates the Nurture somatic mutations of GATA 1 gene cause acute megakaryoblast leukemia and results in the formation of transient abnormal myelopoiesis (Roberts I 2014).

The patients with Diamond-Blackfan anemia, Shwachwan-Diamond Syndrome, severe congenital neutropenia, thrombocytopenia and other BMF Syndromes have increased risk of developing leukemia (Alter BP 2010).

2.4.5.2. Exposition of Leukemia in Down Syndrome:

The frequency rate of leukemia is higher in children with trisomy 21, hence directly promotes the hematological malignancy. DS is not a definite genomic instability syndrome consequently the risk of developing solid tumours, Wilms-tumour and neuroblastoma are rare in these patients (Hasle H 2001). DS neonates have the risk 10 to 20 times higher chances to develop acute leukemia with the normal leukemic childhood population, (Hitzler JK 2003). In children with DS the age and onset of disease progression will be on negotiation manner and Acute leukemia subtype classified. The children with older than 4 years they may develop ALL and whereas below 3 years prone to develop acute megakaryoblastic leukemia (AMKL) with 500 times more when compare without DS children (Hitzler JK 2003; Lange B 2000).

Another form of clonal transformation which affects 5 to 10% of population of DS known as transient myeloproliferative disorder (TMD), it's condition where the accumulation of Megakaryoblasts in fatal liver and peripheral blood and an undisguised condition of Acute leukemia mostly TMD considered as a preleukemic condition and will occurs spontaneous remission with 3 months of early period with 59 to 64% variation (Kanezaki R; Massey GV 2006).

Hence 20% children's with TMD may develop AMKL in the first 3 years of life after the remission of TMD and it could get revert with only chemotherapy. Mutations of GATA 1 gene in the second exon 5! End leads to the high progression of TMD and AMKL and whereas at the exon 3 is less.

The GATA 1 gene, JAK 3, JAK2 and TP53, FLT3 gene frequencies and abnormalities have been listed in the table (Queiroz LB 2001).

Table-2.1. Genomic variations of leukemia with DS.

S.no	Leukemia Type	Gene name	Cytogenic location	Frequency %
1	AMKL	GATA 1	Xp11.23	89.2%
		JAK 3	19.p13.1	13.2%
		JAK2	9p.24.1	6.2%
		TP53	17p.13.1	21.4%
		FLT3	13q.12.2	5.7%
2	TMD	GATA 1	Xp11.23	97.3%
		JAK3	19.p13.1	12.5%
		TP53	17.p13.1	7.7%

2.4.6. Neurological problems:

Down syndrome patients are prone to develop early onset Alzheimer's Disease (AD). And the Development of Dementia at the age 50 in the DS patients with a prevalence range of around 70% (Holand AJ 2000; Janacki MP 2000; Jonasen P 1996) some genetic variants play a critical role in developing early onset AD. Which are known to be the Amyloid Precursor Protein (APP), Apolipoprotein E (APOE), beta secretase 2 (BACE2), Phosphatidylinositol binding Clathrin assembly protein (PICALM). Previous studies demonstrate that a tetranucleotide tripeptide ATTT at intron 7 in the APP protein causes early onset AD in DS population.

2.4.7. Gastro intestinal problems:

Down Syndrome patients prone to develop duodenal stenosis (DST) 260 times and whereas Imperforate anus (IA) 33 times higher and 12% chance of getting Hirschsprung's Disease (HD), with the normal population (Holand AJ 2000; Berrocal T 1999). The Gastro intestinal problems include constipation and irritable bowel Syndrome, haemorrhoid's, Anal fissures, anal fistulas, peripheral infections and several other. Among which constipation and Irritable bowel Syndrome are most common. Previous studies suggest that, HD is caused by a mutation in the DSCAM (Down Syndrome cell adhesion molecule) gene it's expressed in neural crest and enters into the nervous system (Berrocal.T 1999).

AIM AND OBJECTIVES

3. AIM AND OBJECTIVES

3.1 Aim

The main aim of the present study is to identify the Secondary complications associated with Down syndrome.

3.2. Objectives:

1. Phenotypic and genotypic identification of individuals with Down syndrome

2. Identification of secondary complications in Down syndrome by studying the risk of development of;
    i. Diabetes and Cardiovascular complications
    ii. Thrombophilic complications
    iii. Hematological malignancy or Leukemia

3. Clinical correlation of identified molecular abnormalities with phenotype

MATERIALS & METHODS

4. MATERIALS AND METHODS

A total of 70 patients with Down syndrome were included in this study after obtaining informed consent. An equal number of healthy individuals, without any medical complications, were also recruited after their consent and these healthy individuals were served as control subjects in this study.

4.1. Inclusion and exclusion criteria

Patients with known phenotype of Down Syndrome who are diagnosed by cytogenetic studies were included in this study. Patients with congenital abnormality, other than the confirmed Down Syndrome, such as Turner's Syndrome, Zellweger Syndrome were excluded from the study.

4.2. Sample preparation:

Five ml of peripheral blood was drawn using 21 gauge needle in a vacutainer tube containing citrate. Further to that, the sample was centrifuged at 1,000 x g for 15 minutes and the supernatant was collected without disturbing the pellet and freeze and stored at -80°C. Serum samples were used wherever required in this study. For the genotypic identification of Down syndrome, cytogenetic analysis was carried out by following the standard procedures. Briefly, 3 μl of blood was incubated with culture media at 37 degree Celsius for 72 hours and proceed with several steps, including incubation in culture media, harvesting, staining and visualizing for any chromosomal abnormalities.

4.3. Phenotypic and genotypic identification of individuals with Down Syndrome:

4.3.1. Phenotypic identification: Down Syndrome phenotypic features is analyzed with the help of genetic consultants and Physicians. Down syndrome patients have various clinical features, among which are common and as per the proforma includes the following 21 features.

Microcephaly, Brachycephaly, Flat Occiput, Wide Open fontanelle, Flat facial profile, Dysplastic, low-set ears, Epicanthic folds, Upward slant of Palpebral fissures, Squint, Short & broad neck, Short & broad hands, Small fingers, especially 5th, Simian crease, Clinodactyly, Dysplastic middle phalanx of 5[th]finger, Increased gap bet 1 & 2 toes, Furrow on sole, Hypotonia, Hyper extensibility, Hyper flexibility, Heart murmur.

4.3.2 Genotypic Identification: The genetic identification of Down Syndrome includes various techniques such as Fluorescence in Sensitive Hybridization (FISH), Karyotyping, Quantitative Fluorescence Polymerase Chain Reaction (QF-PCR), Multiplex Probe Ligation Assay (MLPA), Next generation Sequence (NGS) and Paralogous sequence quantification (PSQ) these techniques thoroughly reviewed (Asim A 2015). Among which our lab routine Karyotyping protocol has used.

4.3.2.1. Karyotyping protocol:

4.3.2.1.1. Sample collection: Take fresh blood (within 2 hours after the sampling) in the heparin (Anticoagulant) vial or take commercially available heparin and add 2 to 3 μl of heparin in the collection tube.

4.3.2.1.2. Culture: Add 10 ml of ready to use media or fresh media to 0.5 ml of heparin blood. And then keep it for 69 to 72 hours at 37^0 C for cell division.

4.3.2.1.3. Harvesting: Add 200μl colchicine to the media (to arrest the cell cycle at Metaphase stage. And then Harvest at 37^0C for 1 hour. And centrifuge for 10 mins at 1000 rpm. Discard the supernatant, to the pellet add Kcl (to swell the cell) and incubate for 20 mins at 37^0C. Centrifuge at 1000 rpm for 10 mins.

Then again remove the supernatant to that pellet, add 5 drops of fixative (Methanol & Acetate) within the 3:1 ratio. Remove the supernatant, then add fixative and keep it at 37^0C for overnight.

4.3.2.1.4. Washing: Wash the overnight sample 3 times with fixative.

4.3.2.1.5. Slide preparation: Add 2 to 3 drops of cold fixative (Methanol & Acetate) to the tube, add drop the cells on slide at 45^0 angles. Heat the slides at the 45^0C. And mark the slides. Keep the slides at 80 to 90 ^{0}C for overnight.

4.3.2.1.6. Banding:

Take 0.70 g Nacl in 100 ml Milli q water. (0.85%) and then keep it in the 4^0C for 1 to 2 hrs. Take the Methanol with Coupling Jar and keep for 1 hour. And then take 3 coupling jars, with one in trypsin and dip it for 6 to 8 Sec, another two washes with D.H_2O for 2 mins, in each coupling jar.

4.3.2.1.7. Staining Giemsa Satin: Giemsa Satin commercially available

4.3.2.1.8. Buffer preparation:

Disodium Phosphate (Na$_2$HPO$_4$) 3.12 grams in 100 ml Sterile D H$_2$O,

Potassium Bi Phosphate (KH2PO$_4$) 2.84 grams in 100 ml D.H$_2$0 M mix it and adjust the pH 6.8 to 7.2.

4.3.2.1.9. Staining preparation:

Take 5 ml Disodium Phosphate (Na$_2$HPO$_4$) and 5 ml Potassium Bi Phosphate (KH$_2$PO$_4$) make up to 100 ml with D.H$_2$O. And add 5 ml of Giemsa Stain Commercially available. Add the stain to the slides.

4.3.2.1.10. Mounting & Screening of Slide: Add 3 drops of DPX media on the slides and cover with coverslip. And keep for overnight at room temp. Cytogenetic Analysis can be done and made a report.

4.4. Identification of secondary complications:

4.4.1. The risk of development of Diabetes and Cardiovascular complications:

The early prediction of such complications will help implementing preventive measure which will eventually enhance the societal practices and quality of life of individuals with DS. To assess the risk of diabetes and cardiovascular defects by measuring the levels of peptides that are related to cardiovascular diseases, obesity and diabetes mellitus, Bio-Plex Pro Human Diabetes panel was used as per the previous studies (Meena AA 2020). The panel included C-Peptide, Ghrelin, Gastric Inhibitory Polypeptide (GIP-1), Glucagon Like Polypeptide (GLP-1), Glucagon, Insulin, Leptin, Plasminogen Activator Inhibitor-1 (PAI-1), Resistin and Visfatin. The following flow chart represents main steps involved in this procedure

4.4.1.1. Overall Flow chart:

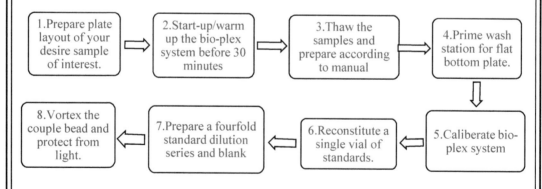

Figure-4.1. Bio plex flow chart.

Table-4.1. Platelet layout of 96 well plate.

	1	2	3	4	5	6	7	8	9	10	11	12
A	Blank	Blank	S8	S8	DS 14	DS28	DS 41	DS 48	DS 53	D-L-1	C5	C13
B	S1	S1	S9	S9	DS 14	DS28	DS 41	DS 48	DS 53	D-L-1	C6	C14
C	S2	S2	S10	S10	DS 15	DS31	DS 43	DS 49	DS 54	D-L-2	C7	C15
D	S3	S3	DS 3	DS 7	DS 15	DS31	DS 43	DS 49	DS 54	D-L-2	C8	C16
E	S4	S4	DS 3	DS 8	DS 18	DS35	DS 44	DS 50	DS 55	C1	C9	C17
F	S5	S5	DS 4	DS 8	DS 18	DS35	DS 44	DS 50	DS 55	C2	C10	C18
G	S6	S6	DS 4	DS 12	DS 23	DS39	DS 45	DS 52	DS 57	C3	C11	C19
H	S7	S7	DS 7	DS 12	DS 23	DS39	DS 45	DS 52	DS 57	C4	C12	C20

38

4.4.1.3. bio-plex adipokine measurement protocol:

The sample preparation was done by diluting 20μl of serum sample with 60μl of Bio-plex human serum diluent. adipokine standard was diluted in the standard diluent – diluted standard, this solution was kept ice for 30 minutes.

Followed by this step, 4-fold serial dilutions of Adipokine standard were done. The 80μl of standard diluent was taken as blank.

The bead preparation was done by diluting the 575μl of 10 X beads in 5175μl of assay buffer and wrapped it with aluminum foil to avoid the exposure to light.

The 50μl of bead was added to all 96 well followed by the addition of 50μl of blank, standard and sample accordingly and incubated in the shaker at 850 rpm for 30 minutes at 25°C.

In the intervening period, streptavidin PE was prepared by mixing 60μl of SAPE with 5940μl of assay buffer.

This solution was vortexed and 50 μl was added to each well followed by incubation at 850 rpm for 10 minutes.

The washing was done in-between every step. The 125μl of assay buffer was added to all wells and incubated at 850 rpm for 30 seconds.

Finally, the plate was placed on the Bio-plex micro-plate platform for adipokine estimation and values that showed co-efficient of variability (CV).

4.4.1.4. Statistical Analysis:

Statistical analysis was applied using SPSS v.16. Mann Whitney U test was carried out to establish the normality of the distribution of continuous variables. One-way analysis of variance (ANOVA) followed by Dunnett's post hoc tests were carried out to evaluate the differences among the study subjects and controls. The effect of each categorical variables (i.e., obesity, cardiovascular disease and diabetes in DS) on continuous variable (i.e., individual peptide level) and statistical significance of the differences in the frequencies of qualitative variables were evaluated using Pearson's v2 test. Pearson correlation coefficients were calculated to describe the associations of plasma adipokines with metabolic complications of individuals with DS and healthy subjects (univariate analysis).

4.5. Risk of development of thrombophilic complications:

Thrombophilia can be defined as predisposition to develop thrombosis and this can either be inherited or acquired. The interconversion of Homeostasis in to Pro coagulation condition results in (uncontrolled blood clot) Thrombosis or this condition is known as Thrombophilia. Methylene Tetra Hydro Folate Reductase (MTHFR) plays a major role in thrombophilia by influencing the folate metabolism, with the property of DNA methylation and nucleotide synthesis. MTHFR 677 C>T variation is one of the confined genetic risk factors for the DS.

Factor V Leiden 1691 G>A and Prothrombin 20210 G>A variations are also frequently associated with Venous Thrombo Embolism along with MTHFR 677 C>T. The aim of this study was to identify thrombophilic complications in patients with DS.

4.5.1.DNA Isolation:

DNA isolation can be done by using Manual Phenol- Chloroform Isoamyl alcohol method.

4.5.1.1. Reagents Required:

> 1X ELB (Erythrocyte lysis buffer) PH-8.

> Proteinase K (20mg/ μl).

> Phenol (Tris-equilibrated phenol).

> Chloroform.

40

- Iso- amyl alcohol

- TE buffer

- Ethanol

- 20% SDS.

4.5.1.2. Preparation of Chemicals:

4.5.1.2.1. Erythrocyte Lysis Buffer (ELB):

It consists of 155 mM ammonium chloride, 723 mM potassium carbonate, and 0.5M EDTA dissolved in 1L of distilled water PH adjusted to 8, it lyses RBCs.

4.5.1.2.2. 20% SDS:

20g of SDS is dissolved in 100ml of distilled water, it is an anionic detergent.

4.5.1.2.3. Proteinase K:

20 mg of proteinase k is dissolved in 1ml of autoclaved distilled water.

4.5.1.2.4. Phenol:

Phenol is saturated with an equal volume of Tris (pH 8.0) until a pH of 8 is obtained. Liquefied phenol is a clear, colourless liquid and can be used for molecular work without Reinstallation. Crystalline phenol is not recommended as it must be redistilled at 60°C to remove oxidation products such as quinone that causes breakdown of phosphodiester bond or causes cross linking of RNA and DNA.

4.5.1.2.5. 1M Tris:

121.14 g of Tris base is dissolved in 900 ml water the pH is adjusted to the dissolvedvolume by adding conc. HCL. The pH of Tris solution is temperature dependent and decreases approximately by 0.03 pH for every 1°C rise in temperature. The solution is allowed to cool in room before making final adjustments to pH the volume is adjusted to 1L with distilled water and sterilized by autoclaving.

4.5.1.2.6. *Chloroform-isoamyl alcohol*:

Chloroform and isoamyl alcohol are mixed in ratio of 24:1. Iso-amyl alcohol is frequently used to remove proteins from nucleic acid and also reduces foaming during extraction.

4.5.1.2.7. *Absolute ethanol*:

100% Ethanol serves as absolute ethanol.

4.5.1.2.8. *70% ethanol*:

70 ml of ethanol is made up to 100ml with distilled water.

4.5.1.2.9. *TE buffer (pH 8)*:

10 mM Tris-Cl P^H 8, 1 mM EDTA. Make from 1M stock of Tris-Cl (pH 8.0) and 500 mM stock of EDTA (pH 8.0) i.e., 10ml 1M Tris-Cl PH 8 per L and 2ml 500mM EDTA

4.5.1.2.10. *Equilibration of phenol:*

Before use, phenol must be equilibrated to a pH>8 because the DNA partitions into organic phase at acid pH. Store liquefied phenol at -20^0C. As and when needed remove the phenol from freezer and melt it at 68^0 C. Add hydroxyquinoline to final concentration of 0.1%.

This compound is an antioxidant, a partial inhibitor of RNAse and a weak chelator of metal ions. To the melted phenol, add an equal volume of Tris buffer (0.5 M Tris, pH 8.0). Stir the mixture on a magnetic stirrer to 15min. Two phases are formed upper aqueous phase and lower organic phase. The upper phase has removed with the help of the glass pipette attached to a vacuum device. Add equal volume of 0.1M Tris to the phenol. Stir the mixture on the magnetic stirrer for 15min. separate the aqueous phase with a pipette attached to a vacuum. Repeat the extraction until the pH of the phenolic phase is >7.8 and stored at 40 C until use.

4.5.1.3. *Principle*:

Genomic DNA was isolated from whole blood in anticoagulant (EDTA) by using the standard proteinase K, Phenol–chloroform procedure. Digestion of blood sample with Proteinase K will prepare a crude lysate by digesting cellular proteins. SDS is used to break the disulphate bonds. Phenol is used to reduce the proteins. Chloroform facilities the separation of aqueous phase and organic phase. Isoamyl alcohol reduces foaming during extraction. Ethanol helps to precipitate DNA and remove the remaining salts.

4.5.1.4. Procedure:

- ➢ 2ml of blood sample was mixed with 6ml of ELB and incubated for 15minutes at -20°C.
- ➢ After incubation the mixture was centrifuged at 6000 rpm for 5 minutes.
- ➢ Step 2 was repeated until the pellet turns white. 16µl of proteinase K and 120µl of SDS was added.
- ➢ The mixture was then incubated overnight at 37°C.
- ➢ After incubation 2ml of phenol was added and centrifuged at 12000 rpm for 10 minutes
- ➢ The organic layer was removed and to the aqueous layer 1ml of phenol and 1ml of chloroform- isoamyl alcohol were added and centrifuged at 12000 rpm for 10 minutes.
- ➢ Again, the organic layer was removed and to the aqueous layer 2ml of chloroform isoamylalcohol was added and centrifuged at 12000 rpm for 10 minutes.
- ➢ The supernatant was collected in a Falcon tube.
- ➢ 100% chilled ethanol was added to the mixture (Fig.36) and incubated overnight at -20°C.
- ➢ After incubation the mixture was centrifuged at 3000 rpm for 10 minutes
- ➢ The DNA from the falcon tube was collected in 1.5ml eppendorf tube and 70 % ethanol was added then centrifuged at 3000 rpm for 10 minutes.
- ➢ This step was repeated 3 times by adding 70% ethanol.
- ➢ The supernatant was discarded and the pellet was allowed to dry in the room temperature.

- After the pellet gets dried up dissolved in 50 to 200µl of TE buffer and kept overnight at 4°C.

- Then quantified the DNA concentration both quality and quantity by using the Nano drop The DNA was stored at -20°C.

- Visualize the DNA bands by using 0.8% Agarose Gel Electrophoresis.

4.5.1.5. The overall flow chart of DNA Isolation:

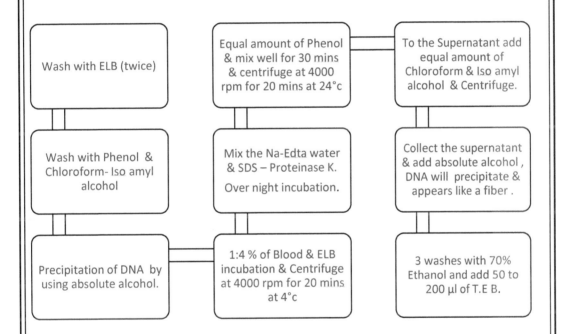

Figure-4.2. DNA Isolation protocol flow chart.

4.5.2. Thrombophilic Genes:

4.5.2.1. MTHFR (Methylene Tetra Hydro Folate Reductase) Gene:

MTHFR gene is a key regulatory enzyme in folate and homocysteine metabolism. Cytogenetic Location: 1p36.22. a total of 34 rare but deleterious mutations. MTHFR 677C→T (A222V) genotype could be implicated as a maternal risk factor for septal defects especially in children with DS these are the Forward 5'TGAAGGAGAAGGTGTCTGCGGGA 3' and Reverse primers 5'- AGGACGGTGCGGTGAGAGTG 3 have been used. The amplicon size is 198 base pairs and Hnif-1 restriction enzyme is used to digest.

4.5.2.2. FVL (Factor V Leiden) Gene:

FVL gene located on chromosome *1q24.2,* and it's having 25 exons. In exon 10 a single point mutation where Adenine replaces Guanine at position 1691 and formation of Glutamate to Arginine at the position of 506. Resulted protein prevent the cleavage of Factor V by APC, results the inactivation and clotting process become less prohibited. Forward & reverse primers 5'-CATGAGAGAACATCGCCTCTG 3' & 5 ' GACCTAACATGTTCTAGCCAGAAG-3' have been used and the amplicon size is 147 base pairs, Mnl-1 restriction enzyme is used to for digestion.

4.5.2.3. Prothrombin Gene:

Located on chromosome *11p 11- q 12*. Having 14 exons and separated by 13 introns with the 5 prime upstream untranslated (UT) region and 3 prime UT region, G to A transition at 20210 position which plays a major role in gene expression. Increases the plasma prothrombin levels and increases the Venous Thrombo Embolism complications. And the primers forward 5'-TCTAGAAACAGTTGCCTGGC-3' and reverse 5'-ATAGCACTGGGAGCATTGAAGC-3'have been used, the amplicon size is 345 base pairs and the Hind III enzyme is used for digestion. The experimental procedures (Kannan M 2019) as from the previous studies.

Table-4.2. Following PCR master mix has been used for all the PCR experiments.

S.NO	Components	Units /Volume
1	Nuclease Free Water –	18.125 μl
2	10X Buffer	(10X) – 2.5μl
3	d NTP mix	(100μm) – 0.5 μl
4	Forward Primer	(10μm) – 0.125 μl
5	Mgcl2	(25mM) – 1.5 μl
6	Reverse Primer	(10μM)– 0.125 μl
7	Taq Polymerase	(1.25 U) – 0.125
8	Template DNA	40 (Nano grams) 2 μl
	Total	25 μl

Table.4.3. Temperatures used for PCR methods.

S.no	Name of the step	Temperature	Time
1	Initial Denaturation	94° C	5 mins.
2	Primer denaturation	94° C	1 min
3	Annealing	59.5° C	1 min
4	Extension	72 ° C	1 min.
5	Number of cycles	30	
6	Final extinction	72 ° C	10 mins

Table-4.4. RFLP master mix

S. No	Name of the Component	Units /Volume
1	Nuclease free water	8 µl.
2	10 X Buffer(10X)	(10X)2 µl
3	HINF-1 Restriction Enzyme	(10 U) 1 µl
4	Amplified Product	10 µl
	Total volume	21 µl

For the RFLP the mixture was kept at 37° C for overnight

After completion of the PCR and RFLP the amplified and restriction digestion products separated by using Agarose gel electrophoresis. The gel concentration is 2%. And the samples were loaded on the each well by 10 µl of PCR product along with 2 µl of 6X Loading dye. And run it for 40 min at 88 volts. The 50 kb & 100 kb Markers (Ladders) was added for the reference.

4.6. Risk of development of hematological malignancy (Leukemia):

Exome sequencing was utilized complex diseases such as cancer, diabetes, obesity and other pathogenic genes using specially designed probes to enrich the protein coding region of interest. High-throughput sequencing generated genetic information, which greatly improved the efficiency of exome studying and significantly reduced the cost of research.

4.6.1. Sample DNA Grouping Quality Assessment

Table.4.5- sampling codes & types used in the NGS.

S.NO	Sample Type	Sample Code
1	Non-Leukemia	DS-3 and DS-30
2	Leukemia	DS-ALL-1 and DS-ALL-2

The liquid chip capture system (Agilent, CA, USA) is used to efficiently enrich the human exon region. High throughput sequencing is performed on the HiSeq 2500/4000 platform. Construction and capture experiments are carried out using the Sure, Select Human All Exon V6 kit (Agilent, CA, USA).

The amount of DNA to be $>= 1.5$ ug (Qubit) and agarose gel electrophoresis result should show no degradation and no RNA contamination. The amount of OD260/280 measured by Nanodrop should range from 1.8 to 2.0. DNA amount < 1 ug, a substitute protocol may be suggested for optimizing the sequencing library.

Table-4.6. following table represents various tools used in NGS.

S.NO	Analysis	Tool
1	Data Quality Control	Fast QC (A quality control tool for high throughput sequence data)
2	Mapping	BWA (Burrows-Wheeler Alignment)
3	Preprocessing of mapped data	SAM tools (suite of programs for interacting with high-throughput sequencing)
4	Preprocessing of mapped data	Picard (set of command line **tools** for high-throughput sequencing data)
5	SNP/INDEL Detection	GATK (genomic analysis toolkit identifying SNPs and indels in germline DNA and RNA seq data).
6	SNP/INDEL Annotation	VEP-Ensemble (Variant Effect Predictor determines the effect of your variants (SNPs, insertions, deletions, CNVs or structural variants).

Good quality reads were mapped to the reference genome using BWA (Burrows-Wheeler Alignment) Tool. BWA is a software package for mapping low-divergent sequences against a large reference genome, such as the human genome. It consists of three algorithms: 1) BWA-backtrack, 2) BWA-SW 3) BWA-MEM.

The BWA-backtrack is designed for Illumina sequence reads up to 100bp, while the rest two for longer sequences ranged from 70bp to 1Mbp. BWA-MEM and BWA-SW share similar features such as long-read support and split alignment, but BWA-MEM, which is the latest, is generally recommended for high-quality queries as it is faster and more accurate. And also has better performance than BWA-backtrack for 70-100bp Illumina reads.

4.6.2. Experimental work flow

Genomic DNA is randomly broken into small 150-300 bp fragments. Following end-repair and poly adenylation at both ends, the fragments are ligated with the sequencing adaptor including specific indices. The library is then hybridized with up to 738,690 biotin-labeled probes so that the exon region (including the upstream and downstream regions) of 58 Mb can be captured using streptomycin beads. After PCR amplification and quality assurance, the library is loaded on the flow cell for sequencing (Figure). Paired-end reads (2 x 150) are obtained for downstream data analysis.

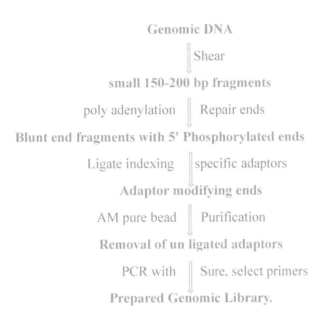

Figure.4.3. NGS overall flow chart.

4.6.3. Experimental analysis:

After marking duplicate reads, it is necessary to re-align the reads close to the region reported as insertion/deletion (INDEL) by BWA. The mismatch close to the INDEL region reported by BWA may not be accurate due to its algorithm of alignment and it may cause false positive results of variant calling. Therefore, correction at these sites is required for subsequent SNP and INDEL analysis. Additionally, the sequencing quality at the 3' end is always lower than the quality at the 5' end due to reagent depletion, and the quality of A/C is often lower than

T/G. Therefore, it is necessary to recalibrate the base quality using the Base Recalibrate module in GATK so the quality score of the sequence can be more reliable.

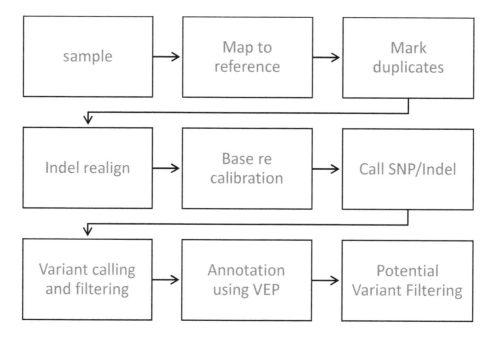

Figure.4.4. NGS Flow chart.

The Indel Re aligner module in GATK is use to carry out INDEL re-alignment in an effort to minimize the error rate of mismatches near each INDEL site.

Variant calling relies heavily on the quality score of each base reported by the sequencer. After the steps, variant calling is made by the Unified Genotyper. In general, real mutation sites are clustered together by the variant calling model. Therefore, the Variant Re calibrator module in GATK uses a Gaussian mixture model to correct the false positive calls and find the true mutation sites. It is well known that mutations in the coding region may be critical and cause diseases. Therefore, it is important to annotate the biological function of the mutation site. We used the VEP program to examine structural changes at the mutation site and further sort out the candidate area leading to the disease.

4.6.4. *Validation:*

4.6.4.1. Tp53 gene:

Tp53 gene, detected to be abnormal by NGS, was chosen to (i) validate the observed results and (ii) analyze the similar defects in other patients with DS. The TP53 is gene is located on chromosome 17q13. Several polymorphisms have been identified within the *TP53* gene, both in non-coding and coding regions.

One of most common SNPs of the *TP53* gene is *72 Arg/Pro (rs1042522)*. The *TP53* codon 72 polymorphisms are located in exon 4 with CGC to CCC transition, leading to an Arginine-to-Proline amino acid substitution in amino acid position 72.

Present study was conducted to examine the association between the *P53 Arg72Pro* polymorphism and Risk of Acute Lymphoblastic Leukemia and to assess correlation between P53 Arg72Pro polymorphism and clinical parameter, haematological profile.

4.6.4.2. *Genotyping of TP53 by Allele Specific PCR:* Genotyping of TP53 exon 4 codon 72 Arg/Pro (rs1042522) SNP (rs1042522) TP53 gene was performed by Allele-Specific Polymerase Chain Reaction (AS-PCR), the following primers were used.

Primers for ARG 72 variant = Forward (5'-TCCCCCTTGCCGTCCCAA-3'),

Reverse (5'-CTGGTGCAGGGGCCACGC-3').

Primers for PRO 72 variant= Forward (5'-GCCAGAGGCTGCTCCCCC-3'),

Reverse (5'-CGTGCAAGTCACAGACTT-3').

Table-4.7. PCR master mix for TP53 72 Arg/Pro variant.

S.NO	Name	For 1 reaction	n. no. of samples	Total volume
1	10X Buffer(10X)	2.5 µl(25X)	6	15 µl
2	D NTP Mix (40 µM)10 each	0.5 µl(5µM)	6	3 µl
3	Forward Primer (10 pm)	0.125 µl(0.076 pm)	6	0.75 µl
4	Reverse Primer (10 pm)	0.125 µl(0.067)	6	0.75 µl
5	Mgcl$_2$ (25 mM)	2 µl(50mM)	6	12 µl
6	Taq Polymerase (Enzyme) (5 U)	0.125 µl(1.6 U)	6	0.75 µl
7	Nuclease free water	18.625 µl	6	111.75 µl
8	DNA	1 µl(30 to 40 ng)		144 µl

RESULTS

5. RESULTS

5.1. Study subjects:

A total number of patients for this study includes 70 among which, 45 are males and 25 are females and their age ranged between 2 months and 18 years. Clinical features and karyotyping have been performed for all the 70 patients. And some of the patients have going through some complications like Congenital Heart defects, and few of are diagnosed with leukemia and with very large number of patients have diagnosed with developmental delay, and some of the patients are difficulty in walking, hence we have included all these subjects based on their Clinical phenotype and Karyotyping Reports.

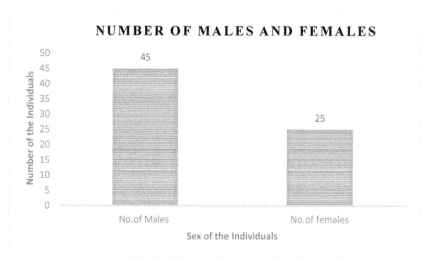

Figure-5.1. Subjects of the study

5.2. Phenotype and Genotypic Identification of Down syndrome:

5.2.1. Phenotypic identification:

DS patients have special phenotypic characteristics which include *Microcephaly, Brachycephaly, Flat Occiput, Wide Open fontanelle, Flat facial profile, Dysplastic, low-set ears, Epicanthic folds, Upward slant of Palpebral fissures, Squint, Short & broad neck, Short & broad hands, Small fingers especially 5ᵗʰ, Simian crease, Clinodactyly, Dysplastic middle phalanx of 5ᵗʰfinger, Increased gap bet 1 & 2 toes, Furrow on sole, Hypotonia, Hyper extensibility, Hyper flexibility, Heart murmur.*

These clinical features have been measured in all the patients and most of the patients have shown maximum number of phenotypes. Among which the short fingers and increased gap between first and second tow, flat occiput, flat facial profile and epicanthic folds have recognised.

Here Are some peculiar clinical phenotypes identified for this study.

Here are some peculiar phenotypic characters   a)   b)

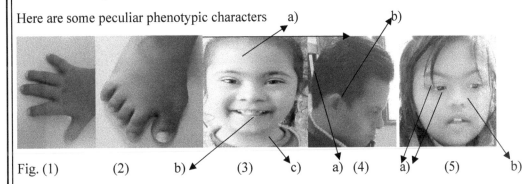

Fig. (1)   (2)   b)   (3)   c)   a) (4)   a)   (5)   b)

Fig.1 Short fingers, (2). Increased gap between first and second tow, (3). a) Wide open fontanelle, b) Upward slant of Palpebral fissures c). Short & broad neck. (4) a) Flat Occiput, dysplastic or smallest years. (5). Flat facial profile a) Epicanthic folds, b) Small or bridged nose.

Figure-5.2. Clinical phenotype identification results.

Among the 70 patients the flat facial profile is 66 patients, upward slant of palpebral fissures is seen in 58 of patients and epicanthic folds and hypotonia both are showing in 57number of the patients. And increased gap in between first and second tow is 56 of patients and whereas the Flat occiput have seen in 54 number of patients, these are the features showing highest number of patients. And the least number of patients shows furrow on sole is seen in 10 patients, squint and high per flexibility has shown in 11 number of the patients. And the remaining features varies from 16 to 40 number of the patients. And the results have been shown in the following bar diagram.

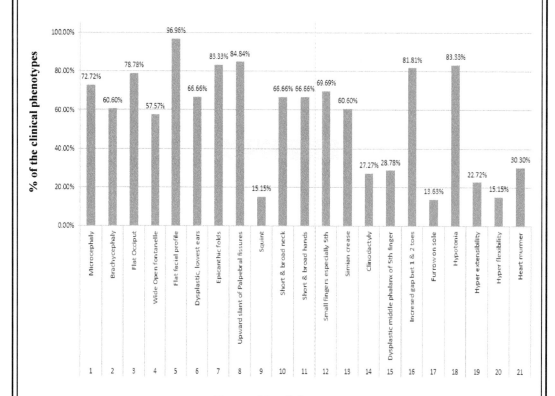

Figure- 5.3. Clinical phenotypic characters

5.2.2. Genotypic Identification:

Genotypic identification carried out by karyotyping method which gives chromosomal alignment and number of the individuals. In this method cultured for 72 hours and given the colchicine treatment to arrest the cell cycle at meta phase stage and Giemsa stain is used for this study and visualisation was good. Ideogram generally is used to identify morphological features of chromosome and it will give diagrammatic representation, by depending on the place of centromere, hence making of chromosomes by decreasing order of their size.

Here the results should show for Down syndrome 47, XX, + 21 or 47, XY, +21. Here DS male represents 47XY and whereas the DS females represent 47XX. In case of normal for

57

male 46, XY and for females 46, XX. The Karyotyping reports have listed in the following images, Down Syndrome and control individuals in the separate imaging reports.

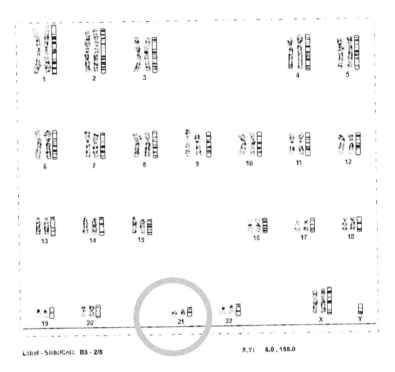

Figure- 5.4. Karyotyping report of Normal individual.

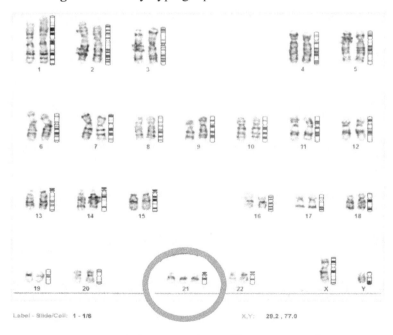

Figure-5.5. Down syndrome Karyotype results

5.3. Identification of secondary complications:

5.3.1. Risk of development of Diabetes and Cardiovascular complications:

Of the 47 subjects who were enrolled in this study, 27 were DS and 20 were healthy controls. Of the 27 DS patients, 16 were males (59.3%) and 11 were females (40.7%). Overall mean age of the DS was 5.7 years with the age ranging between 5 months and 13 years. About 14.8% of our DS had confirmed cardiac-related issues such as congenital heart disease (CHD). Healthy controls' age and sex were similar to that of DS individuals. No significant difference was observed within the DS individuals for the clinical characteristics including age, gender, BMI and duration of the Disease (P>0.053).

Levels of significant adipokines in Down syndrome and healthy controls: The measurement of ten different peptides was carried out in the baseline serum of DS and healthy controls. Table 5.1 summarizes the levels of serum adipokines in study subjects. Of the ten peptides, Ghrelin, GIP-1, GLP-1 and Glucagon levels were significantly higher among DS than in healthy controls (P<0.05). Half of these CHD-associated DS patients were measured low and remaining half measured high for ghrelin when compare to healthy controls. Notably, two peptides, Leptin and Visfatin, were lower in DS than that of healthy controls and the differences were statistically significant (P<0.05). No significant differences were observed for rest of the four adipokines. Of the 6 significant peptides, Leptin showed the unique difference, i.e. the observed levels were very low (<2ng/ml) with the minimum detectable amounts when compared with the normal reference range (2-8ng/ml) and also with the study subjects (8.8ng/ml). The reference ranges of the peptides are listed in table 5.3.

Additionally, when the DS patients were segregated into males and females (Table 2), the serum levels of Ghrelin, GIP-1, GLP-1, Glucagon, Leptin and Visfatin were found to be lower in females than in males. Also, significant differences were observed for GIP-1, glucagon and leptin between males and females (P=0.001). No significant differences were observed for the other three adipokines between male and female study subjects (P>0.05).

Elevated levels of adipokines in the circulation of DS and their association with the disease development: Ghrelin concentration was 1.7 times higher among DS patients when compared to control subjects. Within the DS patients, there was no gender difference observed in postprandial serum ghrelin concentration (P>0.05) and 25.9% of DS were having very low level of ghrelin (below the average of the control) and 66.6% of them had elevated serum ghrelin level. Serum levels of ghrelin were negatively correlated with serum leptin ($r = -0.37$, $P < 0.05$) and insulin ($r = -0.58$, $P > 0.35$). In a stepwise regression analysis, insulin was a significant independent determinant of ghrelin, explaining R=0.36 and adjusted R^2 was 30% (variance), respectively. GIP circulating serum levels were observed to be 1.9 times higher among DS than in healthy controls (1088 vs 569 pg/ml). Within the DS, serum levels of males for GIP were elevated (1283pg/ml) when compare to that of females (804 pg/ml) and this difference was statistically significant (P<0.01). About 11% of the DS patients were having very low level of GIP (below the control average) and 89% of them had elevated serum GIP level.

Next to GIP, the circulating level of serum GLP-1 was observed to be slightly high among DS than in control subjects (386 vs 271 pg/ml). About 44% of the DS patients had very low level of GLP-1 (below the average) and 56% of them had higher level serum GLP-1, but not the elevated level.

We observed significantly higher mean levels of glucagon (p<0.01) in individuals with DS when compared to control subjects (2775 vs 2528 pg/ml). Also negative correlation of postprandial serum glucagon was observed with postprandial insulin levels, explaining R=0.12 and adjusted R^2 was just 12% (variance). Among the DS, as observed with GIP-1, the

60

serum glucagon levels were higher among males than that of females and the difference was statistically significant. About 22% of the DS had very low level of Glucagon-1 (below the average) and 78% of them had higher level glucagon, but not the elevated level.

According to our findings, serum visfatin was higher among healthy controls than the DS patients (8399 vs 8275 pg/ml). When the DS individuals were segregated into males and females, the visfatin levels were slightly higher than the females with DS, but showed no statistical significance ($p>0.13$). Compare to the healthy control, 93% of the DS were very low for circulating visfatin. Similar to visfain, serum leptin levels were recorded as very less among DS, when compared to healthy controls (2256 vs 8840 pg/ml) (Figure). When the DS individuals were segregated in to males and females, the female individuals showed 2.3 times higher levels of leptin compared to that of the males.

The identified serum adipokines between the males and females are shown significant variation. The Ghrelin, GLP-1 and Visfatin values are slightly higher in the DS male patients when compare with Female DS patients. As well as Glucagon values are moderately higher in DS Males than in Female DS patients. And the GIP and Leptin values are highly differing in DS males when compare with female DS cases.

The normal reference ranges of elevated adipokines have taken from the literature, the Ghrelin reference range is 300 Picograms/ mole (Pop.D. et.al. 2015), the GIP normal reference values are 260 to 280 picograms/ mole and whereas the GLP-1 reference range 330 to 350 picograms/ mole (kahles F 2018), Glucagon normal reference ranges are 50 to 100 picograms/ mole (Anoop S 2017), the leptin normal reference range is 2 to 8 nano grams/ mole (Howard JM 2010), and the Visfatin normal reference range is 7.9 nano grams/mole (Farshchian F 2014).

Table-5.1. Serum concentrations of the ten peptides among DS and healthy controls

Analyte	DS Cases (n=27)	Healthy Controls (n=20)	P-Value
C-peptide (pg/ml)	1032±575	647±234	0.381
Ghrelin (pg/ml)	757 ± 485.2	444±134	0.020a*
GIP (pg/ml)	1088± 493.0	569±421	0.0001a*
GLP-1 (pg/ml)	386 ± 115.3	271±29	0.0001a*
Glucagon (pg/ml)	2775± 450.0	2528±153	0.002a*
-Insulin (pg/ml)	535± 325.17	601±485	0.667
Leptin (pg/ml)	2256± 22376	8840±2460	0.0001b*
PAI-1 (pg/ml)	17705±12224	14358±6437	0.796
Resistin (pg/ml)	10818±5453	9795±1121	0.880
Visfatin (pg/ml)	8275.3±6537.5	8299±1705	0.025b*

P<0.05, a-mean ± standard deviation values of cases are higher than control subjects. b*-mean ± standard deviation values of cases are lower than control subjects. Serum levels of the peptides were determined at baseline. Values are expressed as the mean ± standard deviation. GIP-gastric inhibitory polypeptide; GLP-glucagon-like peptide-1, PAI-1- total plasminogen activator inhibitor-1.

Table-5.2. Comparison of serum adipokines between males & females of DS.

Significant Analytes	Males (n=16)	Females (n=11)	P-Value
Ghrelin (pg/ml)	854±560	616±323	0.021*
GIP (pg/ml)	1283± 518	804±283	0.010***
GLP-1 (pg/ml)	418 ± 128	340±77	0.02*
Glucagon (pg/ml)	2955± 485	2514±217	0.009**
Leptin (pg/ml)	1464± 930	3409±3117	0.002***
Visfatin (pg/ml)	9625±8278	6311±1086	0.02*

Values are expressed in mean ± standard deviation, *-significant, ** high significant.

Table-5.3. Normal reference ranges of serum adipokines.

Significant Analytes	Normal range	References
Ghrelin (pg/ml)	300 picograms	Pop D 2015
GIP (pg/ml)	260-280	Kahles F 2018
GLP-1 (pg/ml)	330-350	Kahles F 2018
Glucagon (pg/ml)	50-100	Anoop S 2017
Leptin (ng/ml)	2-8 Nano grams	Howard JM 2010
Visfatin (ng/ml)	7.9	Farshchian F 2014

The markers which have shown the significance when we compare with controls and DS cases have been plotted in the following plot diagrams.

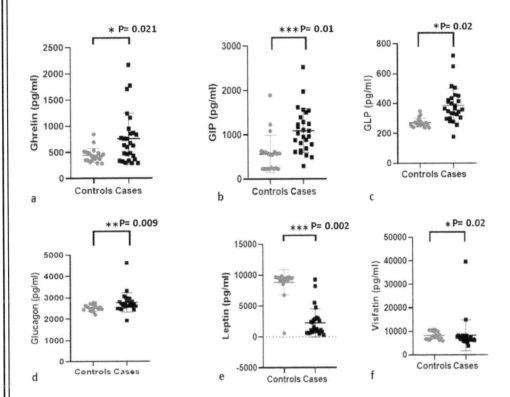

Figure-5.6. Comparison of DS with the controls for the peptides that showed significant alterations. 1a. Ghrelin, 1b. GIP, 1c. GLP, 1d. Glucagon, 1e. Leptin and 1f. Visfatin

The Significant adipokines of Down syndrome cases Mean averages which includes Ghrelin 444.2, GIP 569.2, GLP 271.1, Glucagon 2527.7, leptin 8840, visfatin 8299.8, have been plotted in the following Plot diagram.

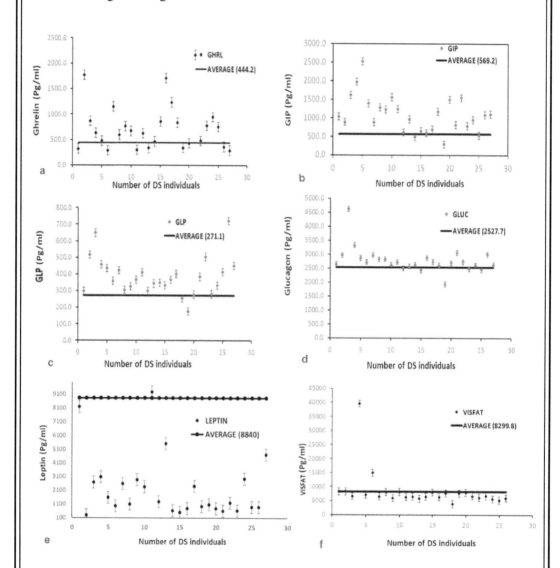

Figure-5.7. Mean average of peptides with significant alterations. 1a. Ghrelin, 1b. GIP, 1c. GLP, 1d. Glucagon, 1e. Leptin and 1f. Visfatin

5.3. 2. Risk of development of thrombophilic complications

5.3.2.1. DNA Isolation:

A total of 140 samples have processed for DNA isolation in which 70 samples are Down syndrome, conformed to karyotyping results. And the 70 healthy control samples without any medical complications and age matched controls. The DNA isolated by using manual Phenol-chloroform & Isoamyl alcohol method. The DNA concentrations with the nanodrop ranges (quantity)1000 μg/μl to 4000 μg/μl. and the (quality) A.260/280% is range 1.78 to 1.9 and whereas the A.260/280 % is 2.1 to 2.4.

Table-5.4. DNA Purity and Concentration ranges

Sample code	DS.1	DS.2	DS.3	DS.4	C1	C2	C3	C55	C56
DNA concentration	1490 μg/μl	1342 μg/μl	1500 μg/μl	1125 μg/μl	1376 μg/μl	1440 μg/μl	2160 μg/μl	782 μg/μl	2334 μg/μl
A.260/280 %	1.85	1.91	1.92	1.81	1.81	1.8	1.83	1.81	1.82
A.230/280 %	2.16	2.13	2.19	2.24	2.36	2.38	2.41	2.24	2.19

Quality of DNA (especially degradation and contamination) have been measured by using 0.8 % Agarose Gel electrophoresis, hence the DNA has not shown any degradation in the gel picture and the quantity of DNA is very high, since we have diluted according to the requirements. We have used 1 Kilo base pair (Kb) marker/ Ladder to check DNA molecular weight of the isolated DNA. The isolated DNA quality have been measured or shown in the following gel electrophoresis images. In which Controls samples and DS samples have run in a separate gel and labelled with separate identification code for this study and the details are listed in the images. The samples have been loaded in the alternative wells.

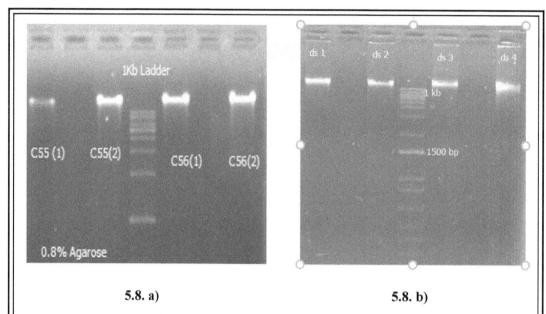

5.8. a)   **5.8. b)**

Figure-5.8. a). 1st and 3rd well contain C-55 (Control samples) and 4th well contains 1 Kilo base pair molecular weight marker/ladder and 5th and 7th wells contains C-56 samples. **b)**. the 1st well loaded with DS-1 (Down syndrome sample), 3rd well loaded with DS-2, 4th well contain with 1Kb ladder, in the 5th well DS-3, and 7th well contain DS-4 samples respectively.

5.3.2.2. Thrombophillic gene variations:

Thrombophillic variations includes MTHFR C 677 T, FVL 1691 G>A, Prothrombin 20210 G>A. These variations have performed with polymerase chain reactions (PCR) and Restriction fragment length polymorphisms (RFLP) methods with different Restriction enzymes.

5.3.2.2.1. MTHFR C667T:

This particular variation performed with PCR in which the amplicon size 198 base pairs. And followed by Restriction digestion with Hinf-1 Restriction enzyme is used to digest in which the heterozygous 198, 175 bp and homozygous samples shown 175 bp have been analysed in the following gel electrophoresis images. In DS patients we have identified 13 heterozygous and 2 homozygous. And whereas in controls we have identified 18 heterozygous mutations and no homozygous mutations have been identified.

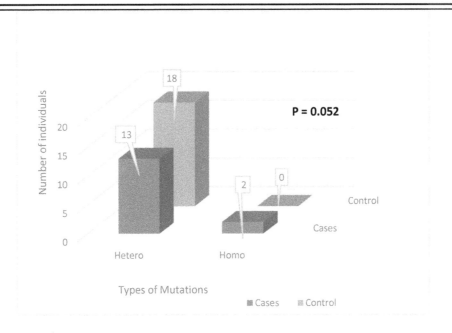

Figure-5.9- MTHFR Gene Variations among DS Vs Controls

5.3.2.2.2. FVL 1691 G>A:

This variation has been performed with PCR in which the amplicon size is 147 base pairs and followed by restriction digestion with Mnl 1 restriction enzyme the digestive bands are 85 and 37 base pairs normal type. Since none of the mutations identified in the DS patients and controls as well in this specific variant.

5.3.2.2.3. Prothrombin 20210 G>A:

The Prothrombin gene Variation performed by PCR the amplicon size is 345 base pairs and RFLP by using Hind III Restriction Enzyme, since none of the mutations have been identified in DS patients and controls as well.

The identified variations include Amplicon sizes and homozygous, heterozygous and normal types are representing in the following gel images with Molecular weight markers/ ladder.

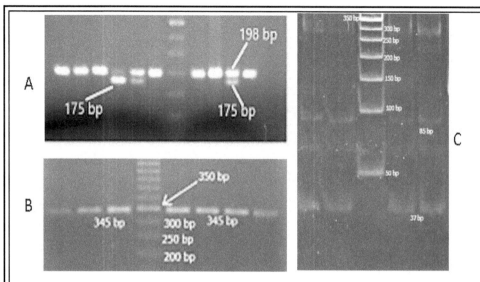

Figure-5.10. Gel photographs showing the results of Factor V Leiden, *MTHFR* C677T and *FII* G20210A. **(A)** Results of *MTHFR* C677T; lanes 1-3 with wide type [198 bp], lane 4 with homozygous [175 bp], lane 5 and 10 with heterozygous [198 bp & 175 bp] and lane 7 was loaded with 50 bp marker. **(B)** Results of *FII* G20210A; lanes 1-3 & 5-8 with wild type [345 bp] and land 4 was loaded with 50 bp marker. **(C)** Results of *FV* Leiden: Lanes 1,2 & 4,5 with wild type [85 bp and 37 bp] and land 3 was loaded with 50 bp marker.

The identified genetic variations have been performed with Odds Ratio with 95% confidence intervals and the P values are measured.

Formulae for this Odds ratio (OR)

$$OR = \frac{Odds\ that\ a\ case\ was\ exposed}{Odds\ that\ a\ control\ was\ exposed}$$

Down syndrome positive and Controls negative = AD

Down syndrome negative and positive Controls= BC

Here we have shown only for MTHFR C66T variation, hence none of the mutations have identified in the FVL 1691G>A & Prothrombin 20210 G>A variations.

Table-5.5. Down Syndrome and controls positive and negative results of MTHFR

	DS cases	Controls
Positive	A=15	B=18
Negative	C=35	D=32

$$OR = \frac{A/C}{B/D} = \frac{15/35}{18/32}$$

$$= \frac{0.42}{0.56} = 0.76$$

The P value helps to hypothesis testing where it eliminates Null hypothesis. And as the low level of P values, it measures the significant results. The obtained results were shown in the following table.

Table-5.6. Genetic Variations and their Odds ratio and P values

Gene Name	Alleles	Cases(N) (%)	Controls(N) (%)	OR (95% CI)	P-value
MTHFR	Normal	35(70%)	32(64%)		
	Heterozygous	13(26%)	18(36%)	0.76 (0.33-1.76)	0.52
	Homozygous	2(4%)	0(0%)		
FVL	Normal	50(100%)	50(100%)		
	Heterozygous	0(0%)	0(0%)	1 (0.02-51.39)	1
	Homozygous	0(0%)	0(0%)		
PTB	Normal	50(100%)	50(100%)		
	Heterozygous	0(0%)	0(0%)	1 (0.02-51.39)	1
	Homozygous	0(0%)	0(0%)		

Normal vs. Heterozygous + Homozygous, OR: Odds Ratio, 95% CI: 95% confidence Intervals.

5.3.3. Risk of Development of Hematological malignancy or Leukemia:

The risk of developing leukemia in a young child is commonly seen in 10 to 20 % of the cases, hence we performed whole genome sequencing technique to identify genetic variants. Exome sequencing refers to the use of specially designed probes to enrich the protein coding region of interest or a specific region of interest. High-throughput sequencing generates genetic information, which greatly improves the efficiency of exome studying and significantly reduces the cost of research. The technology can be used to identify and study Mendelian diseases, complex diseases such as cancer, diabetes, obesity and other pathogenic genes. This enables researchers to better explain the pathogenesis of diseases.

Single Nucleotide Polymorphism (SNP) refers to a single nucleotide variation in the genome which leads to the formation of a genetic marker. Variations at individual nucleotides in the genome include substitutions, deletions, and insertions. Depending on the structure of the nucleotide base, a substitution can be classified into a transition (C to T, G to A) and a transversion (C to A, G to T, C to G, A to T). SNPs appear most frequently in the CG islands. C in the CG islands tends to be methylated during histone modification. Methylated C then turns into T through spontaneous deamination. In general, a SNP refers to a single nucleotide variation with the presence greater than 1% in a population.

SNPs may fall within coding regions of genes, non-coding regions of genes, or intergenic regions. SNPs within noncoding regions may still affect alternative splicing, transcription factor binding, mRNA degradation or non-coding RNA sequences. Gene expression affected by this type of SNPs is known as expression SNP (eSNP) and may occur in the upstream or downstream region of the gene. SNPs within the coding region of the gene (cSNPs) are less common, and the variation rate in the exome is only 1/5 of the variation rate in the surrounding regions. However, they are more significantly correlated to the development of genetic diseases.

5.3.3.1. Sequencing Data Quality Control:

For paired-end sequencing (PE150), the percentage of bases with their quality score greater than 20 should be more than 90%; the percentage of bases with their quality score greater than 30 should more than 85%.

Table. 5.7. Summary of sequencing quality control.

Sample	Q20%	Q30%	GC%
DS-3. fastq	99%	95%	50%
DS-30. fastq	99%	95%	50%
DS-ALL.1. fsastq	99%	95%	50%
DS-ALL.2. fastq	99%	95%	50%

5.3.3.2. SNP Annotation Statistics:

With coding-Non coding sequence (Consequence all) which includes Synonymous variants, missense variant, NMD (nonsense-mediated mRNA decay) Variant, Splice region variants, coding sequence variant and other. Whereas in coding sequence except the NMD variants the remaining all the sequences has shown. The DS and Ds-ALL samples Annotations and SNP's are predicted by VEP (Variant Predictor Effector) tool the SNP's are in the following images. This will vary among one sample to other samples.

5.3.3.3. DS-30 Annotations &S NP's:

Synonymous variants 46%, missense variant 42%, NMD (nonsense-mediated mRNA decay) Variant is 10%, Splice region variants 2%, then remaining variations are present coding sequence variant(all). And whereas in coding sequence Synonymous variants is 52%, missense variant is 47% and stop gained is 1%. The coding sequences with and without NMD variants has shown the following figure.

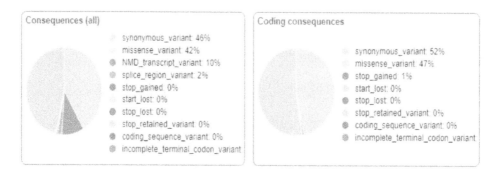

Figure. 5.11. DS-30 Sample Annotations, SNP's predicted by VEP Tool

5.3.3.4. DS-3 Annotations &S NP's:

Synonymous variants 47%, missense variant 42%, NMD (nonsense-mediated mRNA decay) Variant is 9%, Splice region variants 2%, then remaining variations are present coding sequence variant(all). And whereas in coding sequence Synonymous variants is 53%, missense variant is 47% and stop gained and the other coding sequences with and without NMD variants has shown the following figure.

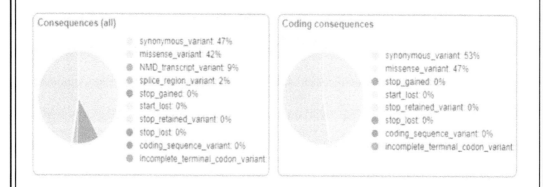

Figure. 5.12. DS-3 Sample Annotations, SNP's predicted by VEP Tool

5.3.3.5. DS-ALL.1. Annotations &S NP's:

Synonymous variants 50%, missense variant 42%, NMD (nonsense-mediated mRNA decay) Variant is 6%, Splice region variants 2%, then remaining variations are present coding sequence variant(all). And whereas in coding sequence Synonymous variants is 54%, missense variant is 45% and stop gained 1% and the other coding sequences are negligible the SNP;s with and without NMD variants has shown the following figure.

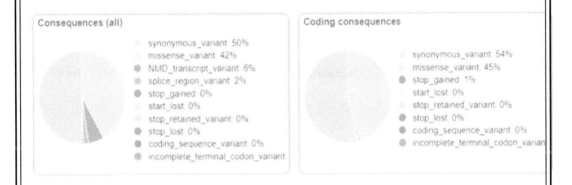

Figure. 5.13. DS-ALL.1 Sample Annotations, SNP's predicted by VEP Tool

5.3.3.6. DS-ALL.2. Annotations &S NP's:

Synonymous variants 47%, missense variant 41%, NMD (nonsense-mediated mRNA decay) Variant is 10%, Splice region variants 2%, then remaining variations are present coding sequence variant(all). And whereas in coding sequence Synonymous variants is 53%, missense variant is 47% and stop gained 1% and the other coding sequences are negligible the SNP; s with and without NMD variants has shown the following figure.

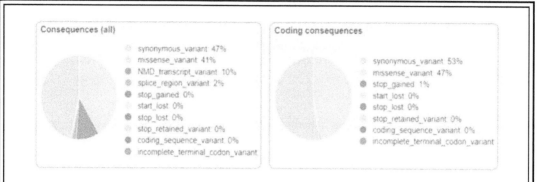

Figure. 5.14. DS-ALL.2 Sample Annotations, SNP's predicted by VEP Tool

SNP and INDEL sites on the genome are analyzed using GATK. After variant calling, Ensemble-VEP command line is used for mutation site annotation. These results in consequence of the mutation in the given genes.

Table.5.8. SNP Results & Statistics

S.no	Parameter	DS-3	DS-30	DS-ALL. 1	DS-ALL. 2
1	Total Number of SNPs / Indels	15266	15038	15226	15769
2	Total Number of SNPs / Indels matched with DBSNPs	14146	13971	13999	14433
3	Novel SNPs / Indels	1120	1067	1227	1336

The following Venn diagram showing 16 genetic variants are common in all 4 samples, which includes Ds-30,3 and DS-ALL.1 and DS-ALL.2. This was predicted by VEP that are related to Acute Lymphoid Leukemia.

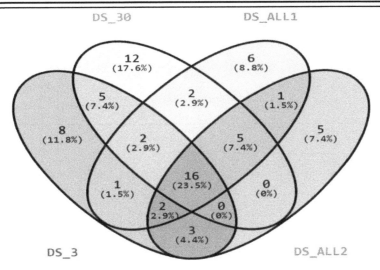

Fighure.5.15. Genetic variants related to ALL published in DBSNP and type of mutation.

The overall mutations identified in all the four samples includes DS-3 have 11 homozygous mutations and 5 heterozygous mutations, DS-30 have 14 homozygous mutations and 2 heterozygous mutations. In the case of DS-ALL.1 the overall homozygous mutations are 12 and 4 heterozygous mutations have identified, whereas in DS-ALL.2 number of homozygous mutations are 10 and heterozygous mutations are 6. These mutations have been shown in the following table.

Table.5.9. The overall homo and heterozygous mutations among the 4 samples.

Sample	Homozygous Mutations	Heterozygous Mutations
DS-3	11	5
DS-30	14	2
DS-ALL-1	12	4
DS-ALL-2	10	6

The common Missense variants predicted by VEP are listed in the following tables. In which Gene name change in A.A sequence and nucleotide change and type of mutations are described.

76

Table.5.10. Variant results Among 4 samples with NGS

S.no	Gene Affecting	Elements	Change in Nucleotide	Effect of variant	Change in Amino acid	Homozygous mutation	Heterozygous Mutation
1	FLT3	rs7338903	28636084G>A	Synonymous Variant	Asp96=	Ds-30, DS-3, D-ALL-1, D-ALL-2	None
2	PDGFRA	rs1873778	55141055A>G	Synonymous Variant	Pro567		
3	PDGFRA	rs7685117	55161391T>C	Synonymous Variant	Asp1074=		
4	PAX5	rs3780135	36840623G>A	Synonymous Variant	Tyr370=		
5	TAL1	rs927462	47685455T>C	Synonymous Variant	Lys311=		
6	CNOT3	rs36665	54649671T>C	Synonymous Variant	Pro243=		
7	PICALM	rs592297	85725937	Synonymous Variant	Gln174=	Ds-30,3,DS-ALL-1	DS-ALL-2
8	*KCNE4	rs12621643	223917983T>G	Missense Variant	Asp196Glu	Ds-30,3,DS-ALL-2	DS-ALL-1

77

					DS-30,3	DS-ALL-1,2
9	IKZF1	rs10899750	50436033A>G	Missense Variant	Arg164Gly		DS-ALL-1,2
10	CNOT3	rs43211	54652203T>C	Synonymous Variant	Gly405=	Ds-30, DS-ALL-1, DS-ALL-2	DS-3,
11	SALL2	rs1263811	21993498G>A	Missense Variant	Pro122Ser		
12	TP53	rs1042522	7579472G>C	Missense Variant	Pro72Arg		
13	NUP214	rs2296710	134021630A>G	Synonymous Variant	Thr617=.	DS-30,DS-ALL-1	DS-3, DSALL2
14	PICALM	rs76719109	85692181A>C	Synonymous Variant	Ala237=		
15	TCF3	rs8140	1619339T>C	Synonymous Variant	Ser434=	None	Ds-30, DS-3, D-ALL-1,2
16	FLT3	rs1933437	28624294G>A	Missense Variant	Thr227Met		

78

Table.5.11. Variant results identified DS-ALL.1 & DS-ALL.2 samples.

S.no	Gene Affecting	Elements	Change in Nucleotide	Effect of variant	Change in Aino acid	Homozygous mutation	Heterozygous Mutation
1	AUTS2	rs2293507	70228020G>T	Missense Variant	Ala303Ser	None	DS-ALL-1
2	AUTS2	rs2293508	70228139A>G	Synonymous Variant	Pro342=	None	DS-ALL-1
3	KMT2A	rs9332801	118355642A>C	Synonymous Variant	Ile1428=	None	DS-ALL-1
4	KMT2A	rs7107305	118368665A>G	Synonymous Variant	Leu1852=	None	DS-ALL-1
5	KMT2A	rs2071702	118373861C>T	Synonymous Variant	Asn2377=	None	DS-ALL-1
6	TCL1A	rs17093294	96178688C>T	Missense Variant	Val56Ile	None	DS-ALL-1
7	TP53	rs3021068	7576630A>C	Missense Variant	Cys341Gly	None	DS-ALL-2
8	TCF3	rs1140828	1619333G>A	Synonymous Variant	Gly436=	None	DS-ALL-2

9	KMT2A	Un-published	118375031G>A	Synonymous Variant	Glu2767=	None	DS-ALL-2
10	ETV6	Un-published	12006478A>G	Missense Variant	His149Arg	None	DS-ALL-2
11	PDGFRA	rs55830582	55141085G>A	Synonymous Variant	Pro577=	None	DS-ALL-2
12	CNOT3	rs42318	54657069C>T	Missense Variant	Ser549Leu	DS-ALL-2	DS-ALL-1

80

5.3.3.7. ValidationTp53 gene:

Tp53 gene, detected to be abnormal by NGS, was chosen to (i) validate the observed results and (ii) analyze the similar defects in other patients with DS. The TP53 is gene is located on chromosome 17q13. Several polymorphisms have been identified within the *TP53* gene, both in non-coding and coding regions.

One of most common SNPs of the *TP53* gene is *72 Arg/Pro (rs1042522),* located on exon 4 with CGC to CCC transition with the result of Arginine to Proline Aino acid substitution associate with the risk of development of Acute Lymphoblastic Leukemia. Pro/Pro genotype increase the risk of ALL.

5.3.8.8. Allele Specific PCR:

Genotyping of TP53 72 Arg/Pro (rs1042522) SNP (rs1042522) TP53 gene was performed by Allele-Specific PCR (AS-PCR). Here are the Arg 72 variants with the DS1,3, 30 and DS-All.1, DS-ALL.2.

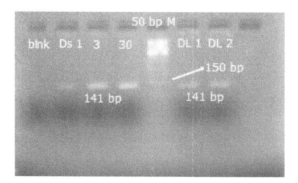

Figure: 5.16. Arginine variant with NGS results,1st well contains blank 2nd DS-1,3[rd] DS-3,4[th] DS-30 and 5th well loaded with molecular weight marker and 6th & 7th wells contain DS-ALL.1 & DS-ALL respectively.

Here we performed DS samples 21 to 30 for the ARG 72 variant among which DS 21,22,24,25,26,27,28,29 samples show positive along with known control DS-30.

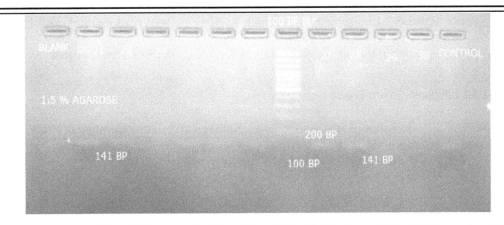

Figure: 5.17. Proline Variant results; 1st well loaded with blank, well 2 to 7 DS samples 21 to 26, 8th well contain molecular weight marker 100 bp,9,10,11 loaded with DS samples 27,28,29 and the 12th well empty and 13th well is loaded with positive control DS-30.

We performed Pro72 variant which is the mutated form of homozygous and it will be normal in case of heterozygous. Here are the results of DS 21 to 30 with positive control.

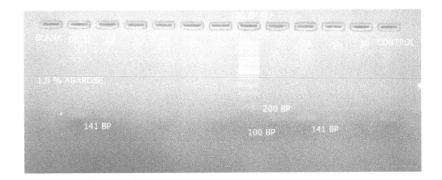

Figure: 5.18. Arginine variant results; 1st well loaded with blank, well 2 to 7 DS samples 21 to 26, 8th well contain molecular weight marker 100 bp,9,10,11,12 loaded with DS samples 27,28,29,30 and the 13th well loaded with positive control.

Here we identified TP53 Pro/Arg variation in 66 DS patients. Among which 23 are ARG homozygous variants which are common in general population and the pathogenic variant PRO

Homozygous variants are found in 19 patients. Heterozygous variants (ARG&PRO) found in 24 patients which are also normal.

Out of 4 DS-ALL samples we found 3 ARG homozygous normal and 1 Pro homozygous and none of the samples have found to be (ARG & PRO) Heterozygous.

Table.5.12. Number of mutations with Genotype.

Type of sample	Number of ARG Homozygous	Number of Heterozygous (ARG&PRO)	Number of PRO Homozygous
Down syndrome	HOMOZYGOUS = 23/66 (34.84%)	HETEROZYGOUS = 24/66 (36.36%)	HOMOZYGOUS = 19 /66 (28.78%)
Down syndrome with Leukemia	3/4 (75%)	0/4	1/4 (25%)

DISCUSSION

6. DISCUSSION

Of 70 patients with DS, 64% were males and 36% were females, Clinical features contribute to the initial diagnosis of the disease among all the DS patients.

Among the 70 patients the flat facial profile is 96.6%, upward slant of palpebral fissures 84.84%, epicanthic folds and hypotonia both are showing in 83.83% of the patients. And increased gap in between first and second tow is 81.81%, Flat occiput have seen in 78.78%, are highest % of patients.

And the least are squint and high per flexibility are 15.15%, furrow on sole 13.63% patients, And the remaining features varies from 72.72% to 27.27% of the patients. Each phenotypic character is differing from one another hence the identification of each Single Nucleotide Polymorphism (SNP) on the Human chromosome 21 helps the understanding of phenotypic variability to genotypic variability (Deutsch G 2001). Hence study demands the understanding of phenotypic characters of each patient. And the results have been shown in the following Pi diagram.

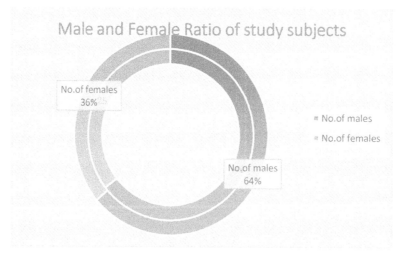

Figure.6.1. Male and Female ratio of the present study

85

Ds Clinical phenotypes +ve %

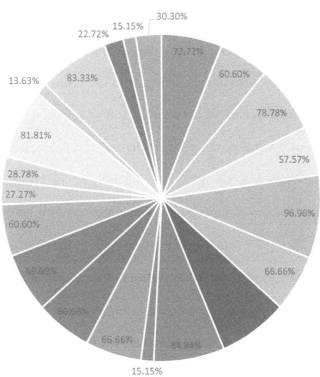

- ■ Microcephaly
- ▫ Flat Occiput
- ▪ Flat facial profile
- ■ Epicanthic folds
- ■ Squint
- ■ Short & broad hands
- ▫ Simian crease
- ▫ Dysplastic middle phalanx of 5th finger
- ▫ Furrow on sole
- ■ Hyper extensibility
- ▫ Heart murmer

- ▫ Brachycephaly
- ▫ Wide Open fontanelle
- ■ Dysplastic, lowest ears
- ■ Upward slant of Palpebral fissures
- ■ Short & broad neck
- ■ Small fingers especially 5th
- ▫ Clinodactyly
- Incresed gap bet 1 & 2 toes
- ▫ Hypotonia
- ▫ Hyper flexibility

Figure.6.2. DS Clinical Phenotype positive %

Despite the earlier detection of DS in utero, new multifaceted and effective medical treatments of congenital heart defects have improved the survival rate of individuals with DS. However, the secondary complications such as obesity, diabetes mellitus and other metabolic complications determine the health status, and thus influence the morbidity and mortality of DS. Improving the earlier interventions may have a long-term benefit on the prevention or reduction of the secondary complications, later in life. The main aim of this objective was to determine the clinical significance of circulating levels of adipokines and other peptides in individuals with Down syndrome. Adipokines, secreted by adipose tissue (AT), are the key regulators of metabolism and they play a significant role in maintaining body weight homeostasis, insulin sensitivity, modulation of immune and inflammatory responses and reproduction (Fantuzzi G 2008). Imbalanced production of adipokines have been associated with metabolic syndromes, cardiovascular diseases and endothelial dysfunction. Recent research has focused much on the potential role of adipokines as biomarkers of metabolism. They serve as crucial factors for the cardiovascular system (Gualillo O 2007). Therefore, in the recent years, there is a growing interest in the potential role of adipokines as biomarkers of low-grade inflammation, obesity and metabolic related cardiovascular complications. The findings of our current study demonstrates that there may be a greater possibility for developing obesity and obesity-related secondary conditions amongst the individuals with DS, which underscores the significant health differences that are present in our study population.

Ghrelin is an important gastric peptide which has growth hormone (GH) releasing effects. In general, the circulating levels of ghrelin shows a peak variation throughout the day and levels remain high (700 pg/ml) while fasting and fall after the ingestion (approximately to 300 pg/ml) (García EA 2006). The relation between the circulating levels of ghrelin with obesity and cardiovascular pathology was elucidated enough, and it was shown to report

87

ghrelin reasons a positive energy balance by limiting the usage of fat and enhancing the intake of food via GH-independent mechanisms (Al Qarni AA 2017; Pinkney J 2014; Pop D 2015). Ghrelin significantly participates in regulating appetite, glucose metabolism, body weight, energy, and fat metabolism and also involves in modulation of cell proliferation/apoptosis, cardiovascular events, gastrointestinal functions, pulmonary and immune functions (Leite-Moreira AF 2017). Also, ghrelin is the most studied new peptide biomarker for obesity and cardiovascular diseases and it can be a potential predictor of the development of metabolic diseases. In our present study, 25.9% of DS were low for ghrelin which suggests higher risk of developing obesity in their near future. On the other hand, ghrelin was reported to have cardiovascular protective effects such as dilation of peripheral blood vessels, protection from ischemia/reperfusion injury, increasing cardiac index and stroke volume, protects cardio myocytes from apoptosis and improving ventricular remodelling (Henriques-Coelho T 2004). About 59.2% of the DS in our study had elevated ghrelin concentration, and these individuals may be protected from the development of cardiovascular diseases, in future.

Of the circulating adipokines measured, ghrelin, GIP, GLP-1 and glucagon were elevated to the greater extent in DS when compared to healthy controls in our present study. These high levels of serum peptides may alarm the development of secondary complications in DS. The low levels of Ghrelin in CHD-associated DS is justified as they have cardiac issues, on the other hand, those CHD-associated DS patients who measured to have elevated ghrelin level could positively help in their prophylaxis and thus may uplift their lifespan. Our hypothesis is strongly supported by the reported evidences that formation of heart tube and development of the embryo heart can be affected by ghrelin or not is controversial, but regular injection of subcutaneous ghrelin 150 µg/kg in chronically hypoxic rats for 14 days significantly attenuates the development of pulmonary hypertension, pulmonary vascular remodelling, right ventricular hypertrophy (Schwenke DO2008).

In recent years, incretin hormones, GLP-1 (glucagon like peptide-1) and GIP (glucose-dependent insulin-tropic peptide) have attained much serious attention as they have a significant role on glucose homeostasis and pathophysiology of other metabolic disorders (Nauck MA 2019). Though GIP and GLP-1 are stepsiblings, they act and exert their effects differently on different tissues and organs. Both GLP-1 and GIP exert their insulin-tropic effect on pancreatic β-cells similarly but act differently in adipose tissue fat deposition. GIP, but not GLP-1, promotes fat deposition at adipose tissues. Literature suggests the correlation of elevated GIP with obesity and GLP-1 with cardio-protective effects such as inhibiting thrombosis preventing atherogenesis protects against vascular inflammation and oxidative stress (Gögebakan O 2015; Khat DZ 2018). In our current study, 89% of the DS showed elevated GIP levels, which suggests the development of obesity in their near future. With respect to GLP-1, 56% of them were having elevated serum GLP-1 levels which is assumed to have protection from cardiovascular diseases at present. The table 5.3 shows the normal reference ranges for both the peptides, GIP and GLP-1 (Kahles F 2018).

Glucagon is a peptide hormone secreted by α cells of the pancreas. The very important role of glucagon is to maintain the glucose homeostasis by thought-provoking hepatic glucose production. Glucagon acts as a glucose mobilising hormone and counter regulator of insulin. Patients with adult obesity and diabetes exhibit increased circulating glucagon in their system. In the present study the levels of glucagon were slightly elevated when compared with the healthy controls (Anoop S 2017). Our current study indicates that 22% of the DS are at high risk for developing obesity. Moreover, it was predicted that chances of developing obesity are possibly more in males compared to females.

Leptin, a 167-amino acid protein, secreted by adipose tissue, regulates energy homeostasis. It exerts pleiotropic effects by binding and activating specific leptin receptors (obR) in the hypothalamus and other organs. Leptin was the first discovered adipocytokine

89

and its circulating concentration was predominantly defined by body fat mass. Leptin is primarily secreted by subcutaneous adipocytes, to some extent in other tissues like visceral adipocytes, placenta, mammary glands, etc., Normal range of the circulating leptin were reported to be 5 to 10 ng/ml in healthy individuals to 40 to 100 ng/ml in obese individuals (Howard JM 2010). A transient increase or decrease in circulation will evoke/bring a reflective change on energy balance and metabolism. It is expected to have increased circulating leptin to proportionate with percent body fat in individuals with DS. However, our study identified very low levels of leptin in DS individuals which may be due to other unexplored causes such as congenital leptin deficiency or other factors as these individuals are prone to have defects in leptin (*LEP*) genes.

Visfatin is a novel adipocytokine, secreted by adipocytes, and is an important endocrine involved in complex network and communicates with different adipocytokines to maintain energy homeostasis and other different biological functions (Mohammadi S 2011). Several reports have attempted correlating circulating visfatin concentration with obesity and found no positive relation between the percent body fat and visfatin concentration (Pagano C 2016; Sun G 2007). Also, Visfatin is involved in early detection of cardiovascular complications (Farshchian F 2014). While, elevated visfatin protects from cardiovascular complications, those DS individuals with less visfatin from our study, may have increased risk of developing thrombotic related complications. Lower visfatin levels have been reported in patients with pulmonary thrombo-embolism (PTE) compared to non-PTE cases adjusted for their BMI (Tutar N 2015). The level was interestingly found to be higher in patients with DVT with PTE, compared to non-DVT cases in the same study.

To conclude, our current study identified the risk of developing secondary complications such as metabolic related defects in patients with DS by using a Bio-pelx panel consisting of multiple adipokines. Out of ten adipokines studied, six were significantly altered in DS patients which suggests the risk of developing secondary complications such as obesity and other metabolic disorders in future. Indeed, this was one among the few studies to improve the quality of life in patients with DS.

We have analyzed the genetic risk factors of *FV*, *MTHFR* and *FII* in large number of patients with DS, with the intent of identifying patients who are potential to develop thrombosis in future. (James SJ 1999) stated that MTHFR 677 C>T variation is one of the confined genetic risk factors for maternal meiotic non-disjunction in DS. And (Zusic-Karic A 2016) shown the frequently recognised mutations of Venous Thromboembolism are MTHFR 667 C>T; FVL 1691 G>A; Prothrombin A 20210 G>A and Protein S and Protein C, Antithrombin III.

Of the three thrombophiic gene variations, MTHFR C677T variation was identified 30% of the patients with DS in the present study.

Though the C677T variation was found to be higher in DS, no significant correlation was identified between the MTHFR C677T and the risk of thrombosis in patients with DS (p= 0.52). With the previous reports the FVL 1691 G>A and Prothrombin G20210A variations are absent when compare with our present study.

16 mutation were common in all 4 sample as predicted by VEP tool.

Among which KCNE4 (rs12621643) was homozygous mutation in DS_ALL-1 and DS-3 and DS-30 sample and heterozygous in DS_ALL-2 which showed the following changes.

The KCNE genes encode small, single transmembrane domain peptides and form a family of regulatory subunits of various Kv channels KCNE4 is an inhibitory subunit to KCNQ1 channels.

There is a correlation between the KCNE4 gene rs12621643 variation and acute lymphoblastic leukemia. With previous studies TP53, FLT3 and JAK2, JAK3, GATA1 gene variations the increased risk of hematoloical malignancy in children with Down syndrome.

Some of mutation were found to be synonymous mutation in coding region, which indicate polymorphism might change the alternative splicing motif and may explain the high frequency of deletions in groups. These synonymous variants associated have shown in the following table.

Table.6.1. Some of the Synonymous Variants with NGS.

S.No	Gene Affecting	Change in Nucleotide	Effect of variant	Change in Aino acid
1	FLT3	28636084G>A	Synonymous Variant	Asp96=
2	PDGFRA	55141055A>G	Synonymous Variant	Pro567=
3	PDGFRA	55161391T>C	Synonymous Variant	Asp1074=
4	PAX5	36840623G>A	Synonymous Variant	Tyr370=
5	TAL1	47685455T>C	Synonymous Variant	Lys311=
6	CNOT3	54649671T>C	Synonymous Variant	Pro243=
7	AUTS2	70228139A>G	Synonymous Variant	Pro342=
8	KMT2A	118355642A>C	Synonymous Variant	Ile1428=

9	KMT2A	118368665A>G	Synonymous Variant	Leu1852=
10	KMT2A	118373861C>T	Synonymous Variant	Asn2377=
11	TCF3	1619333G>A	Synonymous Variant	Gly436=
12	PDGFRA	55141085G>A	Synonymous Variant	Variant Pro577=

Among this, mutation in PAX5 (rs3780135) has been shown to be 90% in population. However, no clinical significance was found to be between with and without ALL.

Based on the above evidence, mutation in KCNE4 is classified as a pathogenic variant. PAX5 shown to be common in all the samples, however is less significant. Based on the literature the TP53 and FLT3 Gene variations are increases the risk of Leukemia especially acute form.

The TP53 ARG 72 PRO variant have shown the significant results in the present study. 28.78% of Down syndrome patients have PRO 72 homozygous mutations these are the pathogenic form and the 34.84% ARG Homozygous mutations are normal individual and the remaining 36.36% are heterozygous (ARG 72 PRO) but normal.

And in case of Down syndrome and Leukemia patients have 25% of the PRO 72 Pathogenic variant and the 75% of patients having normal ARG 72 variant and none of the heterozygous patients were to be found.

Based on the above data the 28.78% of DS patients prone to develop leukemia and whereas DS affected Leukemia patients are 25% having this TP53 72 PRO variation.

CONCLUSION

7. CONCLUSION

Phenotypic and genetic studies play a crucial role in the identification of Down syndrome. In general, the delay in the diagnosis is due to the ignorance of the clinical appearance in children with DS. Thus, it is very important to closely monitor and identify the clinical features of DS, and confirm the diagnosis by genetic study. The significant alteration of adipokines suggests that the DS patients may have a risk of developing complications such as obesity and metabolic defects. The prothrombotic gene variations have no association with the risk of development of thrombosis in DS. Since previous studies have suggested a possible role of homozygous *MTHFR* C677T in the development of thrombosis, our DS patients who were homozygous in this study may not be excluded from the risk of thrombosis. These patients need a special attention and to be monitored for the risk of thrombosis or thrombotic-related complications on follow up. Defects in genes such as KCNE4 and TP53 may serve as markers of leukemia in patients with Down syndrome. The attempt of identifying the secondary complications of DS was one among the few studies to improve the quality of life in patients with DS.

REFERENCES

8. REFERENCES

Anoop, S., Misra, A., Bhatt, S. P., Gulati, S., Mahajan, H., & Prabakaran, G. (2017). High plasma glucagon levels correlate with waist-to-hip ratio, suprailiac skinfold thickness, and deep subcutaneous abdominal and intraperitoneal adipose tissue depots in nonobese Asian Indian males with type 2 diabetes in North India. *Journal of Diabetes Research.*

Antonarakis, S. E., Lyle, R., Dermitzakis, E. T., Reymond, A., & Deutsch, S. (2004). Chromosome 21 and Down syndrome: from genomics to pathophysiology. *Nature reviews genetics*, *5*(10), 725-738.

Al Qarni, A. A., Joatar, F. E., Das, N., Awad, M., Eltayeb, M., Al-Zubair, A. G., ... & Giha, H. A. (2017). Association of plasma ghrelin levels with insulin resistance in type 2 diabetes mellitus among Saudi subjects. *Endocrinology and Metabolism*, *32*(2), 230-240.

Alter, B. P., Giri, N., Savage, S. A., & Rosenberg, P. S. (2009). Cancer in dyskeratosis congenita. *Blood, The Journal of the American Society of Hematology*, *113*(26), 6549-6557.

Alter, B. P., Giri, N., Savage, S. A., Peters, J. A., Loud, J. T., Leathwood, L., ... & Rosenberg, P. S. (2010). Malignancies and survival patterns in the National Cancer Institute inherited bone marrow failure syndromes cohort study. *British journal of haematology*, *150*(2), 179-188.

Aryurachai, K., Archararit, N., Sricote, T., & Angchaisuksiri, P. (2012). Prevalence of factor V Leiden (G1691A) and prothrombin gene mutation (G20210A) Among different ethnic groups in Thai Hospitals. *Journal of Hematology and Transfusion Medicine*, *22*(2), 115-120.

Asim, A., Kumar, A., Muthuswamy, S., Jain, S., & Agarwal, S. (2015). Down syndrome: an insight of the disease. *Journal of biomedical science*, *22*(1), 41.

Bagley, P. J., & Selhub, J. (1998). A common mutation in the methylenetetrahydrofolate reductase gene is associated with an accumulation of formylated tetrahydrofolates in red blood cells. *Proceedings of the National Academy of Sciences, 95*(22), 13217-13220.

Balaghi, M., & Wagner, C. (1993). DNA methylation in folate deficiency: use of CpG methylase. *Biochemical and biophysical research communications, 193*(3), 1184-1190.

Ballard, C., Gauthier, S., Corbett, A., Brayne, C., Aarsland, D., & Jones, E. (2011). Alzheimer's disease. *Lancet (London, England), 377*(9770), 1019-1031.

Bavikatty, N. R., Killeen, A. A., Akel, N., Normolle, D., & Schmaier, A. H. (2000). Association of the prothrombin G20210A mutation with factor V Leiden in a midwestern American population. *American journal of clinical pathology, 114*(2), 272-275.

Berrocal, T., Lamas, M., Gutiérrez, J., Torres, I., Prieto, C., & del Hoyo, M. L. (1999). Congenital anomalies of the small intestine, colon, and rectum. *Radiographics, 19*(5), 1219-1236.

Bergholdt, R., Eising, S., Nerup, J., & Pociot, F. (2006). Increased prevalence of Down's syndrome in individuals with type 1 diabetes in Denmark: a nationwide population-based study. *Diabetologia, 49*(6), 1179.

Beye, A., & Pindur, G. (2017). Clinical significance of factor V Leiden and prothrombin G20210A-mutations in cerebral venous thrombosis–comparison with arterial ischemic stroke. *Clinical hemorheology and microcirculation, 67*(3-4), 261-266.

Bittles, A. H., & Glasson, E. J. (2004). Clinical, social, and ethical implications of changing life expectancy in Down syndrome. *Developmental medicine and child neurology, 46*(4), 282.

Bozikova, A., Gabrikova, D., Pitonak, J., Bernasovska, J., Macekova, S., & Lohajova-Behulova, R. (2015). Ethnic differences in the association of thrombophilic polymorphisms with obstetric complications in Slovak and Roma (Gypsy) populations. *Genetic testing and molecular biomarkers*, *19*(2), 98-102.

Bloomenthal, D., von Dadelszen, P., Liston, R., Magee, L., & Tsang, P. (2002). The effect of factor V Leiden carriage on maternal and fetal health. *Cmaj*, *167*(1), 48-54.

Bull, M. J. (2011). Health supervision for children with Down syndrome.

Christman, J. K., Sheikhnejad, G., Dizik, M., Abileah, S., & Wainfan, E. (1993). Reversibility of changes in nucleic acid methylation and gene expression induced in rat liver by severe dietary methyl deficiency. *Carcinogenesis*, *14*(4), 551-557.

Cicek, M. S., Nock, N. L., Li, L., Conti, D. V., Casey, G., & Witte, J. S. (2004). Relationship between methylenetetrahydrofolate reductase C677T and A1298C genotypes and haplotypes and prostate cancer risk and aggressiveness. *Cancer Epidemiology and Prevention Biomarkers*, *13*(8), 1331-1336.

D'Alto, M., & Mahadevan, V. S. (2012). Pulmonary arterial hypertension associated with congenital heart disease. *European Respiratory Review*, *21*(126), 328-337.

Dahlbäck, B., Carlsson, M., & Svensson, P. J. (1993). Familial thrombophilia due to a previously unrecognized mechanism characterized by poor anticoagulant response to activated protein C: prediction of a cofactor to activated protein C. *Proceedings of the National Academy of Sciences*, *90*(3), 1004-1008.

De Cabo, S. F., Hazen, M. J., Molero, M. L., & Fernandez-Piqueras, J. (1994). S-adenosyl-L-homocysteine: a non-cytotoxic hypomethylating agent. *Experientia*, *50*(7), 658-659.

Degen, S. J. F., & Davie, E. W. (1987). Nucleotide sequence of the gene for human prothrombin. *Biochemistry*, *26*(19), 6165-6177.

Deutsch, G., Jung, J., Zheng, M., Lóra, J., & Zaret, K. S. (2001). A bipotential precursor population for pancreas and liver within the embryonic endoderm. *Development*, *128*(6), 871-881.

Dey, A., Bhowmik, K., Chatterjee, A., Sinha, S., & Mukhopadhyay, K. (2013). Down syndrome related muscle hypotonia: association with COL6A3 functional SNP rs2270669. *Frontiers in Genetics*, *4*, 57.

Dahlbäck, B. (2000). Blood coagulation. *The Lancet*, *355*(9215), 1627-1632.

Duxin, J. P., & Walter, J. C. (2015). What is the DNA repair defect underlying Fanconi anemia?. *Current opinion in cell biology*, *37*, 49-60.

Epstein, C. J., Huang, T. T., Chan, P. H., & Carlson, E. (1990). The molecular biology of Down syndrome. In *Molecular mechanisms of aging* (pp. 98-109). Springer, Berlin, Heidelberg.

Epstein, L. G., & Zin, S. E. (1991). Substitution, risk aversion, and the temporal behavior of consumption and asset returns: An empirical analysis. *Journal of political Economy*, *99*(2), 263-286.

Fantuzzi, G. (2008). Adiponectin and inflammation: consensus and controversy. *Journal of Allergy and Clinical Immunology*, *121*(2), 326-330.

Farshchian, F., Tehrani, F. R., Amirrasouli, H., Pour, H. R., Hedayati, M., Kazerouni, F., & Soltani, A. (2014). Visfatin and resistin serum levels in normal-weight and obese women with polycystic ovary syndrome. *International journal of endocrinology and metabolism*, *12*(3).

Faulks, D., Collado, V., MAZILLE, M. N., VEYRUNE, J. L., & Hennequin, M. (2008). Masticatory dysfunction in persons with Down's syndrome. Part 1: aetiology and incidence. *Journal of Oral Rehabilitation*, *35*(11), 854-862.

Födinger, M., Hörl, W. H., & Sunder-Plassmann, G. (2000). Molecular biology of 5, 10-methylenetetrahydrofolate reductase. *Journal of Nephrology*, *13*(1), 20-33.

Fort, P., Lifshitz, F., Bellisario, R., Davis, J., Lanes, R., Pugliese, M., & David, R. (1984). Abnormalities of thyroid function in infants with Down syndrome. *The Journal of pediatrics*, *104*(4), 545-549.

Freeman, S. B., Taft, L. F., Dooley, K. J., Allran, K., Sherman, S. L., Hassold, T. J., Saker, D. M. (1998). Population-based study of congenital heart defects in Down syndrome. *American journal of medical genetics*, *80*(3), 213-217.

Friso S, Choi SW, Girelli D, Marson JB, Dolnikowski GG, Bagley PJ, Olivieri O, Jacques PF, Rosenberg IH, Corrocher R, Selhub J (2002) A common mutation in the 5,10-methylenetetrahydrofolate reductase gene affects genomic DNA methylation through an interaction with folate status. *Proc Natl Acad* Sci USA 99:5606–5611

Frosst, P., Blom, H. J., Milos, R., Goyette, P., Sheppard, C. A., Matthews, R. G., ... & Rozen, R. (1995). A candidate genetic risk factor for vascular disease: a common mutation in methylenetetrahydrofolate reductase. *Nature genetics*, *10*(1), 111-113.

Garcia, D., Ageno, W., & Libby, E. (2005). Update on the diagnosis and management of pulmonary embolism. *British journal of haematology*, *131*(3), 301-312.

García, E. A., & Korbonits, M. (2006). Ghrelin and cardiovascular health. *Current opinion in pharmacology*, *6*(2), 142-147.

Giannitsis, E., Mair, J., Christersson, C., Siegbahn, A., Huber, K., Jaffe, A. S., ... & Biomarker Study Group of the European Society of Cardiology (ESC) Acute Cardiovascular Care Association (ACCA). (2017). How to use D-dimer in acute cardiovascular care. *European Heart Journal: Acute Cardiovascular Care*, *6*(1), 69-80.

Gilbody, S., Lewis, S., & Lightfoot, T. (2007). Methylenetetrahydrofolate reductase (MTHFR) genetic polymorphisms and psychiatric disorders: a HuGE review. *American journal of epidemiology*, *165*(1), 1-13.

Glasson, E. J., Sullivan, S. G., Hussain, R., Petterson, B. A., Montgomery, P. D., & Bittles, A. H. (2003). Comparative survival advantage of males with Down syndrome. *American Journal of Human Biology*, *15*(2), 192-195.

Gögebakan, Ö., Osterhoff, M. A., Schüler, R., Pivovarova, O., Kruse, M., Seltmann, A. C., ... & Pfeiffer, A. F. (2015). GIP increases adipose tissue expression and blood levels of MCP-1 in humans and links high energy diets to inflammation: a randomised trial. *Diabetologia*, *58*(8), 1759-1768.

Gohil, R., Peck, G., & Sharma, P. (2009). The genetics of venous thromboembolism. *Thrombosis and haemostasis*, *102*(08), 360-370.

Gualillo, O., González-Juanatey, J. R., & Lago, F. (2007). The emerging role of adipokines as mediators of cardiovascular function: physiologic and clinical perspectives. *Trends in cardiovascular medicine*, *17*(8), 275-283.

Haouas, H., Haouas, S., Uzan, G., & Hafsia, A. (2010). Identification of new markers discriminating between myeloid and lymphoid acute leukemia. *Hematology*, *15*(4), 193-203.

Hasle, H. (2001). Pattern of malignant disorders in individuals with Down's syndrome. *The lancet oncology*, *2*(7), 429-436.

Hassold, T., Chen, N., Funkhouser, J., Jooss, T., Manuel, B., Matsuura, J., ... & Jacobs, P. A. (1980). A cytogenetic study of 1000 spontaneous abortions. *Annals of human genetics*, *44*(2), 151-164.

Hassold, T. J., & Jacobs, P. A. (1984). Trisomy in man. *Annual review of genetics*, *18*, 69.

Hassold, T., & Sherman, S. (2000). Down syndrome: genetic recombination and the origin of the extra chromosome 21. *Clinical genetics*, *57*(2), 95-100.

Hassold, T., Hall, H., & Hunt, P. (2007). The origin of human aneuploidy: where we have been, where we are going. *Human molecular genetics*, *16*(R2), R203-R208.

Henriques-Coelho, T., Correia-Pinto, J., Roncon-Albuquerque Jr, R., Baptista, M. J., Lourenço, A. P., Oliveira, S. M., ... & Leite-Moreira, A. F. (2004). Endogenous production of ghrelin and beneficial effects of its exogenous administration in monocrotaline-induced pulmonary hypertension. *American Journal of Physiology-Heart and Circulatory Physiology*, *287*(6), H2885-H2890.

Hitzler, J. K., Cheung, J., Li, Y., Scherer, S. W., & Zipursky, A. (2003). GATA1 mutations in transient leukemia and acute megakaryoblastic leukemia of Down syndrome. *Blood*, *101*(11), 4301-4304.

Holland, A. J., Hon, J., Huppert, F. A., & Stevens, F. (2000). Incidence and course of dementia in people with Down's syndrome: findings from a population-based study. *Journal of Intellectual Disability Research*, *44*(2), 138-146.

Horne III, M. K., & McCloskey, D. J. (2006). Factor V Leiden as a common genetic risk factor for venous thromboembolism. *Journal of Nursing Scholarship*, *38*(1), 19-25.

Horton, A. L., Momirova, V., Dizon-Townson, D., Wenstrom, K., Wendel, G., Samuels, P., ... & Eunice Kennedy Shriver National Institute of Child Health and Human Development Maternal-Fetal Medicine Units Network. (2010). Family history of venous thromboembolism and identifying factor V Leiden carriers during pregnancy. *Obstetrics and gynecology*, *115*(3), 521.

Howard, J. M., Pidgeon, G. P., & Reynolds, J. V. (2010). Leptin and gastro-intestinal malignancies. *Obesity Reviews*, *11*(12), 863-874.

Hua, Y., Zhao, H., Kong, Y., & Ye, M. (2011). Association between the MTHFR gene and Alzheimer's disease: a meta-analysis. *International journal of neuroscience*, *121*(8), 462-471.

Isaacs, H. (2003). Fetal and neonatal leukemia. *Journal of pediatric hematology/oncology*, *25*(5), 348-361.

James, S. J., Pogribna, M., Pogribny, I. P., Melnyk, S., Hine, R. J., Gibson, J. B., ... & Gaylor, D. W. (1999). Abnormal folate metabolism and mutation in the methylenetetrahydrofolate reductase gene may be maternal risk factors for Down syndrome. *The American journal of clinical nutrition*, *70*(4), 495-501.

James, S. J., Pogribna, M., Pogribny, I. P., Melnyk, S., Hine, R. J., Gibson, J. B., ... & Gaylor, D. W. (1999). Abnormal folate metabolism and mutation in the methylenetetrahydrofolate reductase gene may be maternal risk factors for Down syndrome. *The American journal of clinical nutrition*, *70*(4), 495-501.

Jeremiah, D. E., Leyshon, G. E., Francis, T. R. H., & Elliott, R. W. (1973). Down's syndrome and diabetes. *Psychological medicine*, *3*(4), 455-457.

Kabukcu, S., Keskin, N., Keskin, A., & Atalay, E. (2007). The frequency of factor V Leiden and concomitance of factor V Leiden with prothrombin G20210A mutation and methylene tetrahydrofolate reductase C677T gene mutation in healthy population of Denizli, Aegean region of Turkey. *Clinical and Applied Thrombosis/Hemostasis*, *13*(2), 166-171.

Kanezaki, R., Toki, T., Terui, K., Xu, G., Wang, R., Shimada, A., & Ito, E. (2010). Down syndrome and GATA1 mutations in transient abnormal myeloproliferative disorder: mutation classes correlate with progression to myeloid leukemia. *Blood*, *116*(22), 4631-4638.

Kannan M, Yadav BK, Ahmad F, Biswas A, Saxena R (2009) Modulation of clinical phenotype of Glanzmann's thrombasthenia by thrombogenic mutations. Clin Chim Acta 403:156–158

Karlsson, B., Gustafsson, J., Hedov, G., Ivarsson, S. A., & Annerén, G. (1998). Thyroid dysfunction in Down's syndrome: relation to age and thyroid autoimmunity. *Archives of disease in childhood*, *79*(3), 242-245.

Klerk, M., Verhoef, P., Clarke, R., Blom, H. J., Kok, F. J., & Schouten, E. G. (2002). MTHFR 677C→ T polymorphism and risk of coronary heart disease: a meta-analysis. *Jama*, *288*(16), 2023-2031.

Kahles, F., Liberman, A., Halim, C., Rau, M., Möllmann, J., Mertens, R. W., ... & Lehrke, M. (2018). The incretin hormone GIP is upregulated in patients with atherosclerosis and stabilizes plaques in ApoE−/− mice by blocking monocyte/macrophage activation. *Molecular metabolism*, *14*, 150-157.

Khat, D. Z., & Husain, M. (2018). Molecular mechanisms underlying the cardiovascular benefits of SGLT2i and GLP-1RA. *Current diabetes reports*, *18*(7), 45.

Kim, Y. I., Pogribny, I. P., Basnakian, A. G., Miller, J. W., Selhub, J., James, S. J., & Mason, J. B. (1997). Folate deficiency in rats induces DNA strand breaks and hypomethylation within the p53 tumor suppressor gene. *The American journal of clinical nutrition*, *65*(1), 46-52.

Király, A. P., Kállay, K., Gángó, A., Kellner, Á., Egyed, M., Szőke, A., ... & Bödör, C. (2018). Familial acute myeloid leukemia and myelodysplasia in Hungary. *Pathology & Oncology Research*, *24*(1), 83-88.

Kumar, S. I., Kumar, A., Srivastava, S., Saraswat, V. A., & Aggarwal, R. (2005). Low frequency of factor V Leiden and prothrombin G20210A mutations in patients with hepatic venous outflow tract obstruction in northern India: a case-control study.

Kumari B, Srivastava S, Chatterjee T, Vardhan R, Tyagi T, Gupta N, Sahu A, Chandra K, Ashraf MZ (2014) Study of associatedgenetic variants in Indian subjects reveals the basis of ethnicity related differences in susceptibility to venous thromboembolism. Thrombosis 2014:182762.

Kutteh, W. H., & Triplett, D. A. (2006, February). Thrombophilias and recurrent pregnancy loss. In *Seminars in reproductive medicine* (Vol. 24, No. 01, pp. 054-066). Copyright© 2006 by Thieme Medical Publishers, Inc., 333 Seventh Avenue, New York, NY 10001, USA.

Lane, D. A., Mannucci, P. M., Bauer, K. A., Bertina, R. M., Bochkov, N. P., Boulyjnkov, V., & Seligsohn, U. (1996). Inherited thrombophilia: part 1. *Thrombosis and haemostasis*, *76*(05), 651-662.

Lange, B. (2000). The management of neoplastic disorders of haematopoeisis in children with Down's syndrome. *British journal of haematology*, *110*(3), 512-524.

Leclerc, D., Sibani, S., & Rozen, R. (2005). Molecular biology of methylenetetrahydrofolate reductase (MTHFR) and overview of mutations/polymorphisms. *MTHFR Polymorphisms and Disease. Georgetown, TX: Landes Bioscience/Eurekah. com*, 1-20.

Leite-Moreira, A. F., & Soares, J. B. (2007). Physiological, pathological and potential therapeutic roles of ghrelin. *Drug discovery today*, *12*(7-8), 276-288.

Lejeune, J. T. R. G. M., Turpin, R., & Gautier, M. (1959). Le mongolisme, premier exemple d'aberration autosomique humaine. *Ann Genet*, *1*(4), 1-49.

Lettice, L. A., Heaney, S. J., Purdie, L. A., Li, L., de Beer, P., Oostra, B. A. & de Graaff, E. (2003). A long-range Shh enhancer regulates expression in the developing limb and fin and is associated with preaxial polydactyly. *Human molecular genetics*, *12*(14), 1725-1735.

Leung, C., Yeoh, S. W., Patrick, D., Ket, S., Marion, K., Gow, P., & Angus, P. W. (2015). Characteristics of hepatocellular carcinoma in cirrhotic and non-cirrhotic non-alcoholic fatty liver disease. *World Journal of Gastroenterology: WJG*, *21*(4), 1189.

Liew, S. C., & Gupta, E. D. (2015). Methylenetetrahydrofolate reductase (MTHFR) C677T polymorphism: epidemiology, metabolism and the associated diseases. *European journal of medical genetics*, *58*(1), 1-10.

Lucock, M., Daskalakis, I., Briggs, D., Yates, Z., & Levene, M. (2000). Altered folate metabolism and disposition in mothers affected by a spina bifida pregnancy: influence of 677c→ t methylenetetrahydrofolate reductase and 2756a→ g methionine synthase genotypes. *Molecular genetics and metabolism*, *70*(1), 27-44.

Lyle, R., Béna, F., Gagos, S., Gehrig, C., Lopez, G., Schinzel, A., & Antonarakis, S. E. (2009). Genotype–phenotype correlations in Down syndrome identified by array CGH in 30 cases of partial trisomy and partial monosomy chromosome 21. *European Journal of Human Genetics*, *17*(4), 454-466.

Marjot, T., Yadav, S., Hasan, N., Bentley, P., & Sharma, P. (2011). Genes associated with adult cerebral venous thrombosis. *Stroke*, *42*(4), 913-918.

Massey, G. V., Zipursky, A., Chang, M. N., Doyle, J. J., Nasim, S., Taub, J. W., ... & Weinstein, H. J. (2006). A prospective study of the natural history of transient leukemia (TL) in neonates with Down syndrome (DS): Children's Oncology Group (COG) study POG-9481. *Blood*, *107*(12), 4606-4613.

Mégarbané, A., Ravel, A., Mircher, C., Sturtz, F., Grattau, Y., Rethoré, M. O., & Mobley, W. C. (2009). The 50th anniversary of the discovery of trisomy 21: the past, present, and future of research and treatment of Down syndrome. *Genetics in Medicine*, *11*(9), 611-616.

Miletich, J. P., Prescott, S. M., White, R., Majerus, P. W., & Bovill, E. G. (1993). Inherited predisposition to thrombosis. *Cell*, *72*(4), 477-480.

Milunsky, A. (1968). Cystic fibrosis and Down's syndrome. *Pediatrics*, *42*(3), 501-504.

Mohammadi, S., Hosseinzadeh-Attar, M. J., Hosseinnezhad, A., Hosseini, S. H., Eshraghian, M. R., Nezhad, M. K., ... & Karimi, M. (2011). Compare the effects of different visfatin concentration on cardiovascular risk factors, adiponectin and insulin resistance in patients with T2DM. *Diabetes & Metabolic Syndrome: Clinical Research & Reviews*, *5*(2), 71-75.

Nauck, M. A., & Meier, J. J. (2019). GIP and GLP-1: stepsiblings rather than monozygotic twins within the incretin family. *Diabetes*, *68*(5), 897-900.

Nora, E. P., Lajoie, B. R., Schulz, E. G., Giorgetti, L., Okamoto, I., Servant, N., ... & Heard, E. (2012). Spatial partitioning of the regulatory landscape of the X-inactivation centre. *Nature*, *485*(7398), 381-385.

Ornstein, D. L., & Cushman, M. (2003). Factor V Leiden. *Circulation*, *107*(15), e94-e97.

Penrose, L. S. (1933). The relative effects of paternal and maternal age in mongolism. *Journal of Genetics*, *27*(2), 219-224.

Pinkney, J. (2014). The role of ghrelin in metabolic regulation. *Current Opinion in Clinical Nutrition & Metabolic Care*, *17*(6), 497-502.

Pagano, C., Pilon, C., Olivieri, M., Mason, P., Fabris, R., Serra, R., & Vettor, R. (2006). Reduced plasma visfatin/pre-B cell colony-enhancing factor in obesity is not related to insulin resistance in humans. *The Journal of Clinical Endocrinology & Metabolism*, *91*(8), 3165-3170.

Poort, S. R., Rosendaal, F. R., Reitsma, P. H., & Bertina, R. M. (1996). A common genetic variation in the 3'-untranslated region of the prothrombin gene is associated with elevated plasma prothrombin levels and an increase in venous thrombosis.

Peerbooms, O. L., van Os, J., Drukker, M., Kenis, G., Hoogveld, L., De Hert, M., ... & Rutten, B. P. (2011). Meta-analysis of MTHFR gene variants in schizophrenia, bipolar disorder and unipolar depressive disorder: evidence for a common genetic vulnerability? *Brain, behavior, and immunity*, *25*(8), 1530-1543.

Pop, D., Peter, P., Dădârlat, A., Sitar-Tăut, A., & Zdrenghea, D. (2015). Serum ghrelin level is associated with cardiovascular risk score. *Romanian Journal of Internal Medicine*, *53*(2), 140-145.

Prandini, P., Deutsch, S., Lyle, R., Gagnebin, M., Vivier, C. D., Delorenzi, M., ... & Antonarakis, S. E. (2007). Natural gene-expression variation in Down syndrome modulates the outcome of gene-dosage imbalance. *The American Journal of Human Genetics*, *81*(2), 252-263.

Pogribny, I. P., Basnakian, A. G., Miller, B. J., Lopatina, N. G., Poirier, L. A., & James, S. J. (1995). Breaks in genomic DNA and within the p53 gene are associated with hypomethylation in livers of folate/methyl-deficient rats. *Cancer research*, *55*(9), 1894-1901.

Pueschel, S. M., & Pezzullo, J. C. (1985). Thyroid dysfunction in Down syndrome. *American Journal of Diseases of Children*, *139*(6), 636-639.

Queiroz, L. B., Ferrari, Í., de Sá, C. M., Mazzeu, J. F., Magalhães, I. Q., & de Lima, B. D. (2011). Leukemogenesis in Down Syndrome. In *Acute Leukemia-The Scientist's Perspective and Challenge*. IntechOpen.

Readhead, C., Schneider, A., Griffiths, I., & Nave, K. A. (1994). Premature arrest of myelin formation in transgenic mice with increased proteolipid protein gene dosage. *Neuron*, *12*(3), 583-595.

Rees, D. C., Chapman, N. H., Webster, M. T., Guerreiro, J. F., Rochette, J., & Clegg, J. B. (1999). Born to clot: the European burden. *British journal of haematology*, *105*(2), 564-566.

Ridker, P. M., Hennekens, C. H., Lindpaintner, K., Stampfer, M. J., Eisenberg, P. R., & Miletich, J. P. (1995). Mutation in the gene coding for coagulation factor V and the risk of myocardial infarction, stroke, and venous thrombosis in apparently healthy men. *New England journal of medicine, 332*(14), 912-917.

Roberts, I., & Izraeli, S. (2014). Haematopoietic development and leukaemia in D own syndrome. *British journal of haematology, 167*(5), 587-599.

Roizen, N. J., & Patterson, D. (2003). Down's syndrome. *The Lancet, 361*(9365), 1281-1289.

Rosendaal, F. R., Koster, T., Vandenbroucke, J. P., & Reitsma, P. H. (1995). High risk of thrombosis in patients homozygous for factor V Leiden (activated protein C resistance)[see comments].

Roy, A., Roberts, I., Norton, A., & Vyas, P. (2009). Acute megakaryoblastic leukaemia (AMKL) and transient myeloproliferative disorder (TMD) in Down syndrome: a multi-step model of myeloid leukaemogenesis. *British journal of haematology, 147*(1), 3-12.

Schwenke, D. O., Tokudome, T., Shirai, M., Hosoda, H., Horio, T., Kishimoto, I., & Kangawa, K. (2008). Exogenous ghrelin attenuates the progression of chronic hypoxia-induced pulmonary hypertension in conscious rats. *Endocrinology, 149*(1), 237-244.

Sherman, S. L., Allen, E. G., Bean, L. H., & Freeman, S. B. (2007). Epidemiology of Down syndrome. *Mental retardation and developmental disabilities research reviews, 13*(3), 221-227.

Sohn, K. J., Croxford, R., Yates, Z., Lucock, M., & Kim, Y. I. (2004). Effect of the methylenetetrahydrofolate reductase C677T polymorphism on chemosensitivity of colon and breast cancer cells to 5-fluorouracil and methotrexate. *Journal of the National Cancer Institute, 96*(2), 134-14

Sommer, C. A., & Henrique-Silva, F. (2008). Trisomy 21 and Down syndrome: a short review. *Brazilian Journal of Biology*, *68*(2), 447-452.

Svensson, P. J., & Dahlback, B. (1994). Resistance to activated protein C as a basis for venous thrombosis. *New England Journal of Medicine*, *330*(8), 517-522.

Sultan, M., Piccini, I., Balzereit, D., Herwig, R., Saran, N. G., Lehrach, H., & Yaspo, M. L. (2007). Gene expression variation in Down's syndrome mice allows prioritization of candidate genes. *Genome biology*, *8*(5), R91.

Sun, G., Bishop, J., Khalili, S., Vasdev, S., Gill, V., Pace, D., ... & Zhang, H. (2007). Serum visfatin concentrations are positively correlated with serum triacylglycerols and down-regulated by overfeeding in healthy young men. *The American journal of clinical nutrition*, *85*(2), 399-404.

Tabor, A., & Alfirevic, Z. (2010). Update on procedure-related risks for prenatal diagnosis techniques. *Fetal diagnosis and therapy*, *27*(1), 1-7.

Tosetto, A., Missiaglia, E., Frezzato, M., & Rodeghiero, F. (1997). The VITA Project: C677T mutation in the methylene-tetrahydrofolate reductase gene and risk of venous thromboembolism. *British journal of haematology*, *97*(4), 804-806.

Tutar, N., Kemik, N. A., Yılmaz, I., Büyükoğlan, H., Kanbay, A., Dogan, A., & Demir, R. (2015). Is serum cystatin C a predictor of acute pulmonary thromboembolism in patients with normal renal function? *Clinical and Applied Thrombosis/Hemostasis*, *21*(6), 533-538.

Van Cott, E. M., Laposata, M., & Prins, M. H. (2002). Laboratory evaluation of hypercoagulability with venous or arterial thrombosis: venous thromboembolism, myocardial infarction, stroke, and other conditions. *Archives of pathology & laboratory medicine*, *126*(11), 1281-1295.

Van Goor, J. C., Massa, G., & Hirasing, R. (1997). Increased incidence and prevalence of diabetes mellitus in Down's syndrome. *Archives of disease in childhood*, *77*(2), 183.

Wainfan, E., & Poirier, L. A. (1992). Methyl groups in carcinogenesis: effects on DNA methylation and gene expression. *Cancer research*, *52*(7 Supplement), 2071s-2077s.

Wilmer, M., Stocker, C., Bühler, B., Conell, B., & Calatzis, A. (2004). Improved distinction of factor V wild-type and factor V Leiden using a novel prothrombin-based activated protein C resistance assay. *American journal of clinical pathology*, *122*(6), 836-842.

Wiseman, F. K., Alford, K. A., Tybulewicz, V. L., & Fisher, E. M. (2009). Down syndrome—recent progress and future prospects. *Human molecular genetics*, *18*(R1), R75-R83.

Xavier, A. C., & Taub, J. W. (2010). Acute leukemia in children with Down syndrome.

Yahya-Graison, E. A., Aubert, J., Dauphinot, L., Rivals, I., Prieur, M., Golfier, G., & Potier, M. C. (2007). Classification of human chromosome 21 gene-expression variations in Down syndrome: impact on disease phenotypes. *The American Journal of Human Genetics*, *81*(3), 475-491.

Zehnder, J. L., & Benson, R. C. (1996). Sensitivity and Specificity of the APC Resistance Assay in Detection of Individuals with Factor V Leiden. *American journal of clinical pathology*, *106*(1), 107-111.

Milton Keynes UK
Ingram Content Group UK Ltd.
UKHW030951210224
438226UK00011B/224

9 781835 800874